Adolescent & Young Adult Addiction: The Pathological

Relationship to Intoxication and the Interpersonal

Neurobiology Underpinnings

by Jon Daily, LCSW, CADC I

*Introduction (*and chapter, "Neurobiology of Attachment")

by Claude Arnett, MD

Free video presentations from the author at
www.recoveryhappens.com

Adolescent & Young Adult Addiction: The Pathological Relationship to Intoxication and the Interpersonal Neurobiology Underpinnings

Jon Daily, LCSW, CADC II

Left Brain

Right Brain

logic I know exactly who I am
A masters of words and language
Realistic
Always in control
Linear
Analytical
I am order Strategic
I love the familiar
I am logic
I am a scientist
categorize
Control
I am accurate
mathematician
I calculate equations and play
with numbers
practical

I am everything I wanted to be
I am the sound of roaring laughter
A free spirit
I am movement
I sense
I am the urge to paint
on empty canvas
Vivid **I feel**
Art
I am creativity
Poetry
The feeling of sand
beneath bare feet
Yearn
Sensuality
Taste Passion
I am boundless imagination

The eyes can only see what the mind knows.
(Ten years ago, a doctor shared this quote with me, one he valued from his medical school studies.)

Acknowledgments

It is enormously gratifying for me to share my thanks to those who have helped me write this book. Jeff Parrish, thank you for assisting me in the research needed to help develop this work. To the tireless eyes and thoughtful comments from those of you who read this book and provided tremendous feedback for me, Pamela Bouslaugh, Angela Chanter, Debbie Glander, David Gust, Julie Lucas, I truly thank you! To my editor, Virginia McCullough, wow, your insight, inspiration, and guidance really helped carry me. Stacy Lehrer, your cover design and digital formatting is genius. To my colleagues, Curtis Buzanski, Justin Olson, Amy Rose and Rachael Schweitzer at Recovery Happens Counseling Services, and our clients, I learn from you guys daily.

Thanks to David Gust for mentoring me, not only in the field of addiction, but the specialized field of adolescent and young adult addiction. You changed my life. I thank you my friend. To Claude Arnett, if I hadn't met you, this book would not have been written. You have added so much to my thinking about addiction and mental health, which moved me to write this book. I stretched intellectually so much more after knowing you. You also helped to keep this project alive while I was receiving medical treatment for health issues. To my many doctors who treated me and cared for me, know that your care allowed me to finish this work. You have contributed to my field by helping me.

To my friends and family who have loved me and supported me on this journey, I love you! To Dillon and Liberty, my children, I hope this study has helped make me be an even better father to you.

Table of Contents

Introduction

Several years ago I had a moment of enlightenment with Jon Daily. I had invited Jon to my parent education and support group to discuss substance abuse and addiction. At the time, I conducted an intensive outpatient treatment program for teens and young adults with serious mental health problems. I'd worked with most of the parents in my group for many years. Our group discussions largely focused on the way traumatic or neglectful experiences in childhood had manifested in attachment disruption and serious psychopathology in their children.

Jon worked with me in treating a couple of the kids and their families in our program. These particular young people had substance abuse issues. Like most professionals working in "mental health programs," I considered substance abuse a separate problem that, when needed, required additional and separate "substance abuse counseling." We had eighteen people in the group, including parents and two psychologists who worked with me.

That evening, Jon asked a simple question: *How many people here tonight currently have or have had a first degree family member with a serious drug or alcohol problem?* Fifteen hands went up, including mine, with the realization that my brother was addicted to alcohol. Until that moment I had allowed that reality only into the fringes of my consciousness.

I believed I knew most of the parents in my group well, so the discussion that followed surprised me. Parents spoke of *their* parents' alcohol abuse and how it affected their own childhood years. For the first time, a few spoke openly about their own substance abuse, expressing concern about the way it had affected, or currently affected, their children.

During that meeting, Jon educated us about substance abuse and addiction, about denial, preoccupation, and consequences, but also about recovery and hope. Jon's message comes from deeply felt experiences as a teen addict who found his own recovery and today participates in the recovery of others. His message is all about recovery and hope.

As I participated in the discussion, I saw the central connection between substance abuse/ addiction and serious psychological problems. Through many subsequent long, short, and always productive discussions with Jon, I realized how specious the division is between "mental health" and "addiction" or even "dual-diagnosis." I concluded that the majority of individuals, who consistently experience depression, anxiety, paranoia, confusion, loneliness, emptiness, and other painful emotional states, use substances to cope with their pain. They then use denial and deception to hide their shame and attempt to avoid the consequences of their use. And, most importantly, I recognized the disastrous effect that substance abuse and the attendant preoccupation and deception have on interpersonal attunement.

As Jon said that night: *If your time is devoted to preoccupations about when you are next going to get high, or on being intoxicated, or on hiding the evidence of your use, it doesn't leave much time and energy to pay attention to your children, your spouse, and your friends.*

Over the last twenty-five years, the field of psychiatry has focused on the genetic basis of mental disorders. This is a model of mental illness as inevitable, as a deficit from birth that can be treated and managed, but nevertheless must be lived with. As I saw it, the field had lost the *nurture* in the "nature versus nurture" discussion. I had spent the better part of fifteen years reconstructing the logic of our understanding that the experience of disrupted attachment can lead to serious psychopathology such as major depression; bipolar disorder; panic disorder; social phobia; obsessive-compulsive disorder; eating disorders; borderline, narcissistic and schizoid personality disorders; and even brief psychotic disorders.

The entire basis for healthy attachment, the guidance a child needs for healthy emotional and social development, is attunement. With a simple question that burst open the proverbial Pandora's Box, Jon opened me to the realization that much of the lack of the attunement and, therefore, the disrupted attachment we see in our clients, can be significantly attributed to substance abuse. Intoxicated parents, or those preoccupied with either the next chance to become intoxicated or hiding their intoxication, are parents who are not "there" for their children. Likewise, young people—teenagers and young adults—engaged with intoxication are not "there" for their own social and emotional development. Many factors influence disruptions in attachment, including serious trauma, loss of a caregiver, poor emotional "fit" between a caregiver and child, and so forth, but Jon taught me that substance abuse is integrally and inextricably woven into the mix.

The field of substance abuse and addiction has gone through a period similar to what has happened in psychiatry, in that it lost much of the discussion about the influence of nurture. As a field, the focus has been on *using* as the problem. In this paradigm, using stems from a combination of genetic vulnerability and altered neurophysiology from using, and the treatment is to simply stop using. We now see more clearly the inadequacy of this model.

Most substance abusers have multiple forms of intoxication, along with significant social and emotional problems, many of which can be understood by poor regulation of emotion, thought, and behavior. Numerous studies now demonstrate that genetic vulnerability to substance abuse and addiction is similar to genetic vulnerability to depression, anxiety, and other psychiatric disorders, which is simply a higher vulnerability to stress. But even that genetic link is highly influenced by the parenting environment in which children develop.

Jon takes on all these issues in this book. He brings a more thoughtful, inquisitive, personal, and ultimately a greater humanistic perspective to expand our understanding of the use of substances and the myriad social and emotional issues that underlie the problem. He also brought in the field of interpersonal neurobiology to add to our understanding of substance abuse and addiction. Jon discusses the way individuals and families use substances to regulate painful emotional states, an activity or response condoned by our culture. By pointing out our individual and collective preoccupations, denial, deception, and consequences, Jon has helped me to understand substance use and abuse in a broader context. Integral to our social structure, substance use and abuse leads to lack of attunement to our own growth and development and to the growth and development of the people we love and who depend on us.

When young people in my practice present with anxiety, depression, alcohol and/or marijuana use, and occasional cocaine use, I now know, through my collaboration with Jon, that their personal genetic vulnerabilities, their developmental history, *and* the story of their substance use and abuse are crucial to understanding and helping them. I am open to the complexities of their presenting symptoms, emotional traumas, family dysfunction, heritable vulnerabilities, social dysfunction, and the way that substance abuse and addiction are interwoven through all of it. And I see that no way exists to make progress without eliminating or greatly reducing the influence of intoxication on this complex picture. Through Jon's influence, I understand that we cannot build a trusting and helpful relationship with someone whose primary relationship is with intoxication. This has been a revelation in my professional life, in my relationships with family and friends, and in my own personal development.

Today, I am hopeful that Jon's book will provide a similar revelatory experience for professionals, people in recovery, parents, and other interested readers. We need Jon's voice, and others like his, telling us to let go of our preoccupations, denial, deception, and the endless chase for intoxication, and instead, to be here, presenting to and participating with each other and the world around us.

Claude E. Arnett, MD
September 2012

Author's Preface

Not long ago, an acquaintance asked me why I was so excited about writing this book. I had an instant answer: I am passionate about helping people in the grip of addiction, because I know exactly how tight its grip can be. I was once a teenager who struggled with addiction, and because of it, I was kicked out of junior high school, dropped out of high school in the ninth grade, and was incarcerated from ages 15 to 16. I can attribute all these problems and events to my addiction.

I have faced the question about what fueled my addiction, a disease that affects everything in life. With no family history of addiction, how did I get this disease? The addiction was so catastrophic and the recovery so freeing that it brought about my life-long passion to help teenagers and young adults with this illness. Once in recovery, my life lay ahead, but before the first syllabus for my first college class landed on my desk, I'd discovered my purpose and calling.

Eager for the opportunity to learn, better myself, and help young people with addiction issues, I pushed myself from a ninth-grade dropout to being the commencement speaker for my junior college graduation. I went on to graduate with honors from college and graduate school.

During a six-year course of study in psychology and social work, I was never required to take even one course on addiction. An elective course was offered in graduate school, but it was not required. In addition, it focused on adult addiction /alcoholism and never fully examined juvenile onset substance abuse/addiction. Right away, I realized we were way behind in the way we educate professionals and lay people about adolescent addiction, including in the programs designed for those training to become licensed psychotherapists. As a student, I was trained in assessing and diagnosing mental illness as described in the *Diagnostic and Statistical Manual* (DSM IV), which at that time had more pages dedicated to substance use disorders than any other disorder. Further, with all other mental health disorders the assessing clinicians were told they must first rule out a substance use disorder before diagnosing depression, anxiety, personality disorders, schizophrenia, and so forth.

In my senior year of undergraduate work, I shifted away from drug prevention work with preteens and teens to actually treating a broader group of young people (teenagers and young adults) with addiction, along with their families. I did this work at an outpatient program in Fair Oaks, California, and was mentored by my colleague and friend, David Gust, who also is the founder of New Directions. At the same time, I worked at the local psychiatric hospital. After many years in the field it became clear that even after psychiatric treatment, the young people were still addicted. At the same time, 90% of adolescents suffering from addiction have other issues driving their drug problem.

In doing this work, I quickly saw that professionals helping young people often were polarized in their approach to understanding and treating them. Clinicians trained in addiction maintained that drugs caused problems with mood, school, family relationships, overall health, and so forth. Addiction was behind the inability of older adolescents and young adults to make the transition from dependent teenagers to independent young adults going to work or attending college and/or vocational school or enlisting in the military. The addiction specialists working with these young people tended to ignore mental health issues, believing that if the families stopped enabling, then they would break their kids' denial; once the young addict stopped using, all the other issues would clear up.

On the other side, clinicians trained in mental health often took a "kids will be kids and try drugs" approach, while maintaining that underlying issues fueled addiction. Therefore, if the underlying issues were managed, the young users would no longer need the drugs and quit using them. Young people certainly received benefits from each approach, although both schools of thought left areas of addiction and mental health unaddressed.

Trained as an alcohol and drug abuse counselor with a specialty in treating teens and young adults, I'm also a licensed psychotherapist. I found myself talking mostly about mental health issues with my "addiction" colleagues and mostly about addiction with my "mental health" colleagues. Both groups probably thought I was discounting either the addiction or the mental health issues in our clients. However, in reality I compensated for the information my colleagues overlooked on the cases we shared. For years I searched for ways to bridge the knowledge gap between addiction and mental health fields and build a theoretical framework that made sense of both perspectives and could be consolidated into one workable model. This book represents another cobblestone on that road.

Since 1999, the field of interpersonal neurobiology has emerged, with Alan Schore, Dan Siegel, and others leading the way forward. (Interpersonal neurobiology is the neurological science that supports attachment theory, started by the work of John Bowlby.) In their research and writing, I find it amazing that they thoroughly describe addiction without ever once mentioning the word. Making sense of the links of interpersonal neurobiology and addiction requires a complicated journey through the literature. However, it is increasingly clear to me that individuals and addiction are characterized by layers of complexity.

The reality of the complexity adds to my excitement about this book. I believe mental health clinicians will simultaneously feel both validated and challenged to think more comprehensively about adolescent and young adult addiction. Likewise, those in the addiction field will feel simultaneously validated and challenged to think more comprehensively about their understanding and approach to treating young people.

Written at a time when alcohol is still the number one killer of young people, this book examines the impact of adolescent substance use disorders. It is written in the context of a large and growing problem, regardless of the fluctuations in statistics occurring from year to year or decade to decade. For example, the average age of first intoxication is now 12, and not only is marijuana use among teens on the rise again, but the marijuana our teens buy is itself twice as potent as it was 10 years ago and 20 times stronger than it was in the early 1960s. Here in California, many citizens pushed the initiative, Proposition 19, which calls for the legalization of marijuana. Given all these realities, we know for sure that teen addiction is not going to disappear.

I designed this book to address the issue of attachment and addiction from a bio-psycho-social perspective. How does our left-brain dominant, solution focused, and material culture affect the development of a child's brain and mind? How does this driven culture, existing in the information age, create unavailable care givers, relational losses, and unhealthy expectations for our children, even our preschoolers? I address the way parent-child relationships shape how children feel about themselves and their trust in their ability to turn to others for soothing, comfort, and co-regulation. Beyond that, how do parent-child relationships shape the neurological development in a child's brain? We know that shame in early childhood relationships negatively affects the development of the dopaminergic and opiate systems in the brain. In addition, we know that typically abused drugs activate those same systems in the brain. How, then, do we use relationships to activate these systems? Given the current research, how do we as addiction specialists or mental health professionals work with families to help them be biological, psychological, and social resources in children's lives?

In this book, I also make a clear distinction between adolescent- and young-adult onset (juvenile-onset), versus adult-onset substance abuse. For example, teenagers often experience a far more rapid progression from experimentation to addiction than is true for adults. Denial manifests differently, too, in that young people are more likely to glorify their use, while adults are more likely to minimize theirs.

This book also aims to help readers understand the development of secure and insecure attachment, including subset categories of the insecure attachment. As much as possible, I have used anecdotes and vignettes to illuminate how insecure attachment shapes personality, influences affect regulation, increases risk for substance abuse, and influences approach or avoidance of relationships. Because it is a goal in the treatment process, I devote time to discussing the concept of *earned secure attachment*.

Finally, Claude Arnett, MD, brings his extensive knowledge to this book when he eloquently describes the link between attachment and neurological development. What regions and systems develop during the trust versus mistrust stage? How does secure attachment develop neurological regulatory systems and structures in the brain?

Ultimately, I wrote this book to offer clinicians information that brings with it implications for treatment of adolescents, young adults, and their families.

Jon Daily, LCSW, CADC II
September, 2012

Chapter 1

The Adolescent Struggle

Maybe if we are going to invest in drug prevention programs, we need to start with investing in attachment-disorder prevention programs.
-Jon Daily

Early childhood attachment (social) experiences build our biological (bio) and psychological (psycho) capacity to regulate affective states and turn to others for co-regulation. Attachment researchers have theorized that attunement with a stable, responsive caregiver may facilitate children's regulation of attention, emotion, and physiological arousal, hence the term, co-regulation.

In recent years, clinicians treating young people, a group that includes adolescents and young adults, with addictive disorders have become increasingly aware that affect dysregulation and an inability to turn to others for emotional soothing and comfort significantly contribute to the onset of drug use, continued use, and relapse. For sustained recovery to occur, affect regulation should be a significant treatment focus. The challenge for recovering users involves learning to recognize and experience their physiological, emotional, and psychological states, along with understanding their need for support. With this understanding, they can build social support and trust. They can then turn to others to help them regulate their affect states rather than turning to drugs, drug dealers, and drug culture for biological, psychological, and social (bio-psycho-social) soothing. We know from current scientific research that healthy relationships build healthy brains, minds, and social capacities in our developing young people; unhealthy dysregulated brains, minds, and people build dysregulated capacities. This information is the focus of this book.

As preteens enter the adolescent phase of life an internal struggle emerges that can powerfully hijack teenagers' capacity for rational thought and good judgment. Teens in this struggle may have limited ability to use their cortical systems in the brain, i.e., the prefrontal cortex (PFC), which can serve as the *braking/inhibitory system*. This limitation exists because the PFC is not yet fully developed and myelinated. Moreover, the braking/inhibitory system can be hijacked by the subcoritcal structures of the midbrain, the region regulating social and emotional responses and behavior, which we can think of as the *gas pedal/excitatory system*.

These years encompass many social and internal changes. Change, whether good or bad, is a common denominator for stress, and change sums up adolescence in one word. The brain and mind are reorganizing during this last period of *blooming neurons* and the development of the PFC before the early twenties, the time when myelination begins (1) (2) (3) (4). Myelination is the process by which the myelin sheath (insulation/conduit) forms on nerve fibers, typically, around the axon of a neuron. Myelination results in the increased speed of neurotransmission and adds to the stability of the architectural structure of neural networks, making it more difficult to change connections. I often jokingly say: *Older people who are set in their opinions are that way because they are fully myelinated, and this means they come to conclusions faster (speed) and their minds are harder to change (neural network stability).*

This reorganization and the accompanying new experiences result in a struggle as teenagers consider normal questions that accompany adolescence. These include issues of social and personal acceptance, rejection, sexuality, and appearance. Teens often lack both adequate answers to their questions and someone in whom they can confide. In addition, they may be desperate to ameliorate the associated emotions that are unfamiliar or unpleasant, hence the antecedent to drug use.

We all know that adolescence is a turbulent stage of development. During these years young people expand their social networks and try out new and more sophisticated ways of connecting to others and negotiating their relationships. They explore their identity through a reexamination of their values, beliefs, ideas, and behavior. The questions they ask generally include:

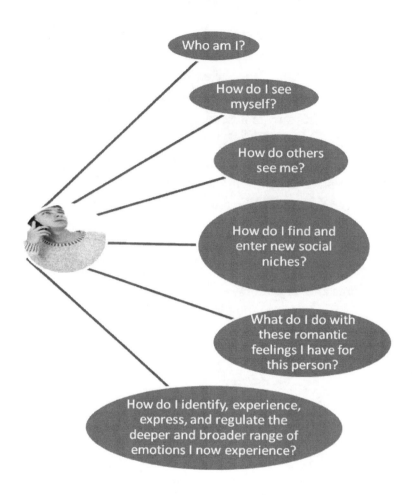

Who am I?

How do I see myself?

How do others see me?

How do I find and enter new social niches?

What do I do with these romantic feelings I have for this person?

How do I identify, experience, express, and regulate the deeper and broader range of emotions I now experience?

These questions are a normal part of development. Moreover, during the second half of adolescence, teens are *supposed* to experience anxiety, even if their lives are proceeding normally. During the first half of adolescence, teens generally are not challenged to think about self sufficiency, because their needs are provided for. They are free to focus on activities like talking on the phone, playing video games, keeping up with their online social networking, skateboarding, and so forth.

However, during the second half of adolescence, teens must face the need to be responsible, accountable, and resourceful as they ponder the future. The questions change, too:

- Will I pass my driver's exam?
- Can I pay for a car?
- Can I afford insurance?
- Can I get a job?
- Do I have what it takes to ask that person out on a date?
- Can I get into college or train for a technical job?
- Which colleges should I apply for?
- Will I be able to support myself after I'm done with my education?

Young people need support during this tumultuous time, but they may have grown up with family issues, relational traumas, poor self-esteem, insecurity, and other mental health issues. The arduous challenge for these teens and young adults is to regulate their emotional state and push to build various competencies and healthy relationships, despite their circumstances and issues.

When does Adulthood Begin?

We often hear that in our society, we have extended adolescence from the late teen years well into the twenties. This has had implications for our society in general, but it is also relevant in a discussion of addiction, because those who become addicted in their teenage years have a difficult time transitioning to young adulthood. For the purposes of this book, we use the term "young people" to include both adolescents and those in their early twenties.

According to Clark, sociologists, psychologists, and others recognize adulthood as starting at age 25, a time when young people typically have graduated from college, entered the military, or are working and can financially support themselves (5). The transition from adolescence to full adulthood means that young adults must assume new social roles and face more complex intellectual and social challenges. However, they face these sophisticated challenges regardless of how well they have worked through previous adolescent challenges, such as identity development, along with physical, social, intellectual, and emotional development. Many young adults face these new challenges while still trying to work through previous social and emotional struggles.

While these young adults are experiencing emerging levels of sophistication in thinking, conflict, tension and emotional regulation challenges, their brains are simultaneously undergoing changes in the regions associated with these necessary capacities for regulation. For example, the prefrontal cortex (PFC) is associated with the ability to plan and anticipate ramifications of decisions, along with the complex concept of morality, authority, civic law, natural law, divine law, and so forth. The PFC is an inhibitory-braking region of the brain that serves to counter the lower subcortical structures of the brain that typically are impulsive-excitatory (limbic and hedonic regions). Translation, a young person who longs for belonging, emotional and social connection, mixed with sexual desire and peer pressure to sneak out of the house while his parents are asleep to satisfy these desires is experiencing impulsive-excitatory drive from the mid and lower regions of the brain (subcortical structures). In this tension filled and primed impulsive state of excitation, the firing of dopamine and other neurotransmitters *ascend* from the lower regions of the brain up to the PFC; here, the PFC can send *descending* signals back to counter this as the young person ponders the morality taught by his parents, culture, and society, thus serving as a inhibitory-braking system. If the PFC dominates in this "tug of war," then he has made the decision to stay home and no risky behaviors or negative consequences occur. If he sneaks out, has sex, and possibly even uses drugs, then he has experienced "bottom up hijacking" whereby the lower regions of the brain have hijacked the top regions. This is the old cartoon depicting the devil on one shoulder, saying, "Come on, it will be fun and your parents will never know." Meanwhile, the angel on the other shoulder says, "You know better than this and when your parents find out they will be hurt and having sex and doing drugs can be harmful."

During the young adult years, we see insulation form around nerve fibers and neural networks, which allows the brain to transmit signals more efficiently. In addition, extra neurons and networks are pruned, which enables those neurons and networks currently used to send signals more efficiently (6) (7). Research has shown that substance use and mental health problems tend to be highest among persons in their late adolescent and young adult years, with substance use generally being higher among males and mental health problems generally being higher among females (8).

We have seen attachment theory research grow over the past sixty years, particularly in the last decade with the advent of research in the field of interpersonal neurobiology. This research demonstrates that children raised by parents who are warm, reflective, consistent, and attuned to their children's needs build the affect regulation system both psychologically and biologically (9) (10). The field of interpersonal neurobiology has deepened our understanding of development by elegantly linking bio-psycho-social variables. In other words, during the last decade, to study attachment theory is to study biology, psychology, and sociology.

In addition, during the last decade, researchers have discovered that systems of the brain and neural networks are developed or stunted as a result of secure or insecure attachment. The development of a child's brain, mind, and affect regulation system is "experience dependent." Specifically, the brain is built and organized from the experiences a child has with caregivers during the early, formative years of life.

Biologically, the opiate and dopamine system fire and develop during the attuned experience between parent and child. A later chapter delves into this neurobiology in greater detail, but briefly, the opiate system helps us manage stress and emotional and physical pain, experience pleasure, and reinforce behavior. Perhaps most significantly, the opiate system is a neurological core component of "secure" human attachment to caregivers in our early childhood experience. As attunement occurs, the system is activated, developing and reinforcing the bond with the caregiver and the associated behaviors involved in approach, such as calling out, walking to, asking for, and so on.

The dopamine system can be thought of as the system of both desire and reward. Dopamine is the central neurochemical in what Panksepp called the seeking system (11). It provides the initial stimulation and excitement for activity and can be thought to set the tone for intensity.

The pleasurable experience of attunement, both biologically and psychologically, reinforces the social attachment between the children and their caregivers. During infancy these systems develop and fire to create a pleasurable experience when the caregiver attunes to the child's needs. As the dopaminergic system and opiate systems are built and firing, the experience of attunement—hedonic—becomes the seeking (desire) and reinforcing (reward) systems. This plays out in the attachment relationship as the child's neurochemistry (bio) reinforces the idea of turning to others (social) for support, affect regulation (psychological), and so forth.

In addition, the attunement experience also builds the child's belief, or Internal Working Model (IWM), that "I can trust others," or conversely, "I can't trust others." (The IWM is explained in detail in a later chapter.) If a child turns to others to be soothed, only to be left alone emotionally, this creates shame (12) (13) or more pain, which thwarts the development of the previously mentioned desire and reward systems, and builds an IWM that represents mistrust and inadequacy of self and others. When this occurs, the IWM reinforces the tendency to turn away from others for support, affect regulation, and so forth. The mistrust of others builds when the act of turning away occurs more frequently than turning to others in search of soothing. Ultimately, unless they can discover relational experiences, mistrusting children are stuck with limited capacity for affect regulation and the ability to build healthy and secure relationships in adolescence and adulthood.

This early bio-psycho-social dynamic underpins and drives addictive disorders. When teenagers are unable to self-soothe, or trust others to help them soothe, then they are at risk for relying on drugs, food, sex, gangs, and so forth, for comfort, and they carry this risk into young adulthood. (These concepts are further developed throughout the book.)

Biologically, almost all addictive drugs activate the dopamine and the opiate system, the same system operating during parent-child bonding in the early years of life. Therefore, drugs become the substitute for healthy regulation and co-regulation from others. Furthermore, young people who mistrust others often quickly discover that drug dealers, and the drug culture in general, respond to their need for closeness, belonging, warmth, and soothing. Drug culture is accepting, not judging; drugs feel intoxicating, not depressing. Currently, many young people play out these struggles in self-destructive attempts to resolve their emotional and social conflicts. When unresolved, these conflicts show up as significant problems in all areas of an adolescent's life and later, in adult life when they attempt to fit in as a member of society.

The Problem of Teen Drug Use

In the office J's mom talks nervously. His dad sits next to her on the couch in a tense silence. Fifteen-year-old J slouches in a plushy chair, almost falling asleep. His mom talks about how she found marijuana in his room six months ago, how they spoke to him and he promised to stop, but his grades continued to deteriorate , his friends changed, he was away from home more, and when he was home they fought constantly. Then J went to outpatient counseling briefly, then to a month-long program for teen substance abusers. But he came back and the same behaviors started again. Now they discovered he is using

Vicodin. She and her husband are scared and do not know what to do. J and his parents are not alone.

Most of us would agree that the number of adolescents using alcohol and illicit drugs is a great concern and many variables contribute to the epidemic. In 2008, the benchmark index, *Monitoring the Future*, an annual survey used by clinicians and researchers to track trends in adolescent drug use, found that 19.6% of eighth graders and 47.4% of high school seniors have used illicit drugs. More specifically, the teens were asked about their near-term use, and *within the past 30 days:*

- **11.2% of eighth graders and 24.9% of seniors tried marijuana;**

- **15.7% of 8th graders and 9.9% of seniors tried inhalants; and finally,**

- **15.9% of 8th graders and 43.1% of seniors have used alcohol.**

This survey also showed that from 1991 to 1999 illicit drug use has nearly doubled (14).

Because of neurological research, we now have a greater understanding of the relationship between early first-use of intoxicants and brain development, along with the subsequent increased risk of addiction. Consider these facts:

- More than 25% (1.8 million) of alcohol-dependent adults, age 21 or older in 2003, first used alcohol before age 14.

- Over 80% (5.1 million) first used alcohol before age 18.

- 96% (6 million) first used before age 21.

(Testimony by Charles Curie, M.A. A.C.S.W, April 26, 2005) (15)

Taken as whole, we can see that on any given day, "100 million Americans are taking some stimulant, antidepressant, tranquillizer, or painkiller; smoking; inhaling from aerosol cans or glue bottles; or self-medicating with alcohol or illegal substances like marijuana, cocaine, heroin, methamphetamines, hallucinogens, Ecstasy, and other designer drugs" (16).

Those of us working in the field also see an additional alarming trend. The total number of drug-using teenagers has increased over the years, and first intoxication occurs at increasingly younger ages. In clinical practice we have seen the average age of first intoxication go from age 15 in the 1980s to age 12 in the late 1990s, an age holding stable in this new century. The decrease in age alarms us because the younger the age at first use, the more likely the individual will go on to develop alcohol or other drug dependency. A study conducted by Dawson and Dawson found that those starting to use drugs at age 13 or younger had a 42% chance of having substance dependence; if they also have a genetic family history of addiction the chance increased by 15% (17).

J's parents are reasonably alarmed. J and other youth are using illicit drugs earlier, experimenting with a wider range of intoxicants, and their repeated use is seriously affecting their social, emotional, and biological growth, which not only disrupts their immediate functioning, but puts them at much higher risk for long-term substance dependence and long-term dysfunction as adults.

More Varied and Potent

Not only have young people begun using alcohol and drugs at an earlier age, we have seen an increase in the variety, potency, and availability of the drugs they typically use. For example, marijuana potency doubled from 1997 to 2008. Is it likely to *decrease* in potency in the future? I doubt it. Today we see technology that enables dealers, growers, and users to produce more potent marijuana in the comfort of their own homes, so to speak. They genetically clone plants and use the latest types of elaborate grow-lighting, technologies that continue to advance. A glance at the chart below reveals the steady rise of marijuana potency.

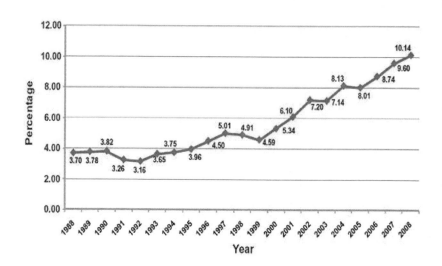

Figure 1. Average Percentage of THC in Samples of
Seized Marijuana, 1988-2008
Source: University of Mississippi Potency Monitoring Project (18)

The Rise in Varied Use

According to a study conducted by Columbia University's
Center on Addiction and Substance Abuse, children who smoke
marijuana are eighty-five times more likely to use cocaine than
their peers who never tried marijuana (19). At our offices in
northern California, we routinely take a drug use history from our
clients. Many years ago, the typical history gathered at an initial
interview consisted of nicotine, alcohol, and marijuana.
Currently, it is increasingly common that these histories list
nicotine, alcohol, marijuana, Ecstasy, mushrooms, nitrous oxide,
Vicodin, hydrocodone, Adderall, and dextromethorphan. Some of
our young clients also report using cocaine, oxycontin,
methamphetamine, salvia, K-2/spice and so forth.

Looking at these lists, it is clear that since the mid 1990s
young people have developed an open mind about what creates
intoxication. This "creativity" takes them beyond the well-
publicized drugs their parents look out for, i.e., cocaine,

36

marijuana, and a few others. Now they search through their parents' medicine cabinet for both psychiatric and over-the-counter medicines. Who would have thought that adolescents would abuse Nyquil, "the sniffling, sneezing, coughing, aching, rest medicine?"

J reported stealing Vicodin from his grandparents' home. He admitted to drinking Robitussin with a friend. He said he had been offered to use cocaine and heroin intravenously, but denied using them. He was familiar with Ritalin, Adderal, Xanax, and Klonopin, though he had never been prescribed any of them. He had tried Ecstacy once, had heard of "G," a designer street drug that reportedly enhances somatic sensations and visual distortions and he states that he wants to try Opana, a strong pain killer.

Emotional turmoil, social pressures, and other issues contribute to drug use, but several common beliefs also play a role. Adolescents often acknowledge negative consequences of using any drug, but then they use false beliefs to justify their use: *It won't happen to me...I can control it... I'll just do it once... I won't use the harder drugs... I can stop any time I want to,* and so on. Logically, negative consequences from drug use occur, and they become the next common denominator for the problems in their lives. In other words, the negative effects of the drugs and drug culture combine with the already present bio-social-psycho issues.

As their relationship to intoxication becomes stronger, their relationship to other areas of life becomes more fragile. Students with a history of good grades begin to fail; they may not graduate, let alone go on to trade school, college or job training or qualify for military service. Some young people gradually reorganize their groups of friends and end up associating only with other drug users. They abandon sports, families, jobs, and other extracurricular activities.

Beyond these consequences, many teens are convicted of serious crimes. We know that the families of young addicts lose many thousands of dollars in attorneys' fees and/or medical bills. Parents often lose time at work while dealing with the consequences of their child's drug issues, and many suffer the demoralizing experience of having their child literally "rip them off." Frankly, many families have lost their children to addiction. Every day, drugs and alcohol drive young people to run away, often disappearing into a community of addicts living on the streets; even worse, drugs and alcohol are a major cause of death of our young people. In recent years, research has illuminated the severity of these consequences.

Consequences: Health

Alcohol, tobacco, and drug abuse is the number one health problem in the U.S., and as such, it places an enormous burden on the country. More deaths, illnesses, and disabilities result from substance abuse than from any other preventable health condition (20). This situation strains the healthcare system and contributes to the death and ill health of millions of Americans every year.

Parents and clinicians working with young drug abusers have witnessed heath issues ranging from things like quitting sports and not getting physical exercise all the way to contracting sexually transmitted disease (STDs), alcohol poisoning and drug overdoses, strokes, and death. In my career thus far, I am aware of far too many adolescents and young adults who have died of addiction-related causes, and many more who have suffered serious injuries from auto accidents, unwanted pregnancies, and violence. In most cases, the fights and other violence would not have occurred outside the presence and use of alcohol or drugs.

In 2006, hospitals in the U.S. delivered patient care in a total of 113 million Emergency Department (ED) visits. The Drug Abuse Warning Network (DAWN) (21) estimates that **1,742,887 ED visits were associated with drug misuse or abuse. Of those ED visits:**

- 31% involved illicit drugs only
- 28% involved pharmaceuticals only
- 7% involved alcohol only in patients under the age of 21
- 13% involved illicit drugs with alcohol
- 10% involved alcohol with pharmaceuticals
- 8% involved illicit drugs with pharmaceuticals
- 3% involved illicit drugs with pharmaceuticals and alcohol

In patients under age 21, DAWN estimates:

- 76,760 alcohol-related ED visits for patients aged 12 to 17
- 105,675 alcohol-related ED visits for patients aged 18 to 20

Alcohol is an illegal drug for both of these age groups. Further:

- About two thirds (69%) of the alcohol-related ED visits for minors involved alcohol and no other drug
- The rate of alcohol-only ED visits for patients aged 18 to 20 (581 visits per 100,000 population) was 2.8 times that for patients aged 12 to 17 (204 per 100,000)
- Males and females had similar rates

Cost to Society

The health and social costs to society of illicit drug use are staggering. Drug-related illness, death, and crime cost the nation approximately $66.9 billion. *Every man, woman, and child in America pay nearly $1000 annually to cover the expense of unnecessary health care, extra law enforcement, auto accidents, crime, and lost productivity resulting from substance abuse* (22).

A 2009 study showed that drug abuse remains one of the top five costliest health problems in the United States. According to a recent report from the National Center for Addiction and Substance Abuse (CASA) at Columbia University (23), most of the money invested in combating alcohol and drug abuse is spent responding to the consequences of these societal problems. Only a minimal 2% percent goes to prevention. The study also found that 96 percent of the $467.7 billion that federal, state and local governments spend on substance abuse is used to deal with the public effects, including crime and homelessness. Healthcare costs associated with substance abuse receive the largest percentage (58.0). Governments spend the second largest percentage (13.1) on the costs of prosecuting and jailing offenders. In a related study from the United States Office of Drug Control Policy, over 50% of men arrested in nine selected cities tested positive for drugs.

As stated earlier, we can all agree that adolescent drug use is of great concern. The open question for parents and therapists is why they use. Parents in our program routinely ask, "What are the underlying issues that make my child *want* to use?" Meanwhile, researchers are trying to answer the same question.

Clinicians usually conclude that as many reasons exist for drug use among young people as there are young people using drugs. For years, researchers have explored this question, and their data shed light on some specific factors. For example, in a study of more than 4,700 teenagers, researchers found that parents' drinking habits appeared to influence their children in both direct and indirect ways. Teenagers seemed to directly follow the example of a parent who drank excessively, or they indirectly viewed their parents' drinking as a sign of lax parenting, which, in turn, affected their likelihood to drink.

Past and current studies have found that parents can be a strong influence on their children's odds of drinking and shed light on how the influence plays out among adolescents (24). Other research shows that a close parent-child relationship, one in which teenagers can turn to parents to discuss their feelings, delays the age of first intoxication.

The Partnership for a Drug-Free America reveals troubling new insights into the reasons teens use drugs. According to the 2007 Partnership Attitude Tracking Study of 6,511 teens (PATS Teens) (25), the number one reason teenagers list for drug use is to deal with the pressures and stress of school. In this nationally projectable study (margin of error +/- 1.6 percent), *73% of teens reported school stress as the primary reason for drug use.* This indicates that teenagers' perceptions of motivating factors for using drugs are dramatically different than past research has indicated.

CHART 1: Leading reasons for using drugs
In 2007 adolescents were significantly more likely to think that *kids use drugs to help with pressures and stress of school* (73%) than they were to view use as a means *to have fun* (26%).

% Agree Strongly/Somewhat

Kids use drugs to deal with the pressures and stress of school	73
Kids use drugs to help them feel better about themselves	65
Kids use drugs to look cool	65
Drugs help kids deal with problems at home	55
Kids use drugs to improve their athletic performance	54
Drugs help you forget your troubles	43
Drug users feel adventurous	48
Marijuana helps you relax	43
Drugs help you lose weight	43
Kids use drugs to improve their physical appearance	43
Being high feels good	40
Drugs help you relax socially	35
Drugs help kids when they're having a hard time	34
Parties are more fun with drugs	26
Drugs are fun	26
Kids use drugs to help them study better	20

As previously stated, the nature of adolescence itself means that young people go through many internal and social struggles. In his formulation of the human hierarchy of needs, Abraham Maslow pointed out attachment is important for both young children and teenagers. However, the kinds of attachments change by adolescence, usually shifting away from caregivers, though the Internal Working Model (IWM) remains, and moves toward peers in the form of the "need to belong." This developmental stage exerts powerful influence and leaves many teens vulnerable to attachments that can lead them down a destructive path and makes it more important that kids go into the high school years with healthy people and resources in their lives, along with, a strong capacity and skill set for coping. The reality is that the teenage and college years will be stressful. That is normal and okay. In fact, more time could be spent by parents and clinicians explaining the normality of it and how to work with and through it. It is a developmental milestone in life.

We know that many stressed and struggling young people feel inadequate in their relationship with themselves, while simultaneously feeling scrutinized by their peers. They will do whatever it takes to be "good enough to belong." Referring to the survey above, you can see that items 1, 3, 4, 5, 9, 10, 12, and 14 are linked to the need to fit in and belong with peers. The powerful drive to keep people close and belong is very real.

Adolescence is a natural time of change and conflict. Teens are discovering their capacity for self-direction. Peter Blos, an eminent specialist in adolescent analysis, once said that teenagers change personalities the way they change clothes. They are trying out new ways to be themselves, new possibilities for who they are and "how they are going to be in the world." This involves a natural amount of self-absorption, risk-taking, and experimentation. Intoxication is often seen as a means to self-exploration, new friends, new perceptions and emotions, and new ways of thinking. The risk of this experimentation is minimized.

Adolescents often acknowledge negative consequences of using drugs and alcohol, but then they use false beliefs and minimization to justify their use: *It won't happen to me…I can control it… I'll just do it once… I won't use the harder drugs… I can stop any time I want to,* and so on. But this new excitement about self-direction and self-control is youthfully naive. Adolescents are largely unaware of the trajectory of their emotional development and how who they have been as young children and as school-age children significantly contribute to their strengths and vulnerabilities and who they can actually become as adults. Logically, negative consequences from drug use occur. And inevitably they interact with and often compound the already existing problems in teens' lives. Then their minimization becomes denial. Experimentation becomes compulsion. A venture into new friends and new feelings becomes a new identity.

Raising adolescents can be challenging and exhausting for parents, too, which often makes it difficult to be emotionally attuned to and supportive of their children's developmental struggles. An accompanying Partnership for a Drug-free America study of parents' attitudes about teen drug use (released in June 2007) showed that parents severely underestimate and are disconnected from the impact of stress on their teens' decision to use drugs. *Only 7% of parents believe that teens might use drugs to cope with stress, despite 73% of teens making that attribution.*

Teenagers struggle and need emotional support and guidance. Affect regulation, a person's ability to manage positive and negative emotional states, is experience dependent. It is not automatic; it is built in the early relationship the child has with its caregiver (26).

Teenagers struggle and need emotional support and guidance. Insecurity in their relationships is going to drive them to soothe unpleasant emotions on their own. Unfortunately, many teenagers discover that drugs can change the way they feel. Drugs can give them the experience of feeling soothed, calm, euphoric, stimulated, and so forth. When it comes to the need to belong, teens have learned that drug culture is responsive to their calls, nonjudgmental, and accepting. In the survey mentioned, nearly all the 16 reasons teenagers give for using drugs can be attributed to managing painful emotions and to the all important need to be accepted in a peer group.

Furthermore, in 2009, a study by the American Psychological Association (APA) was referenced on a blog at the *New York Time's* website about teen stress (27). The blog specifically focused on the disparity between what teens report about the stress they experience, versus what parents believe about their teenagers experience of stress. As author Lisa Belkin says, "Not only are our kids feeling it [stress], we parents aren't noticing."

As another example, almost half of children (ages 8 and up) believe school is stressful, but only one-third of parents see school as stressful to their children. Consistently, parents underestimate the source and intensity of their children's stress. Unbeknownst to many parents, 30% of teens are concerned about the family finances, but only 18% of parents believe this is a source of stress for their teens. Further, both teens (and "tweens," those who are between late childhood and adolescence) report difficulty sleeping and experience headaches in numbers only slightly lower than their parents, yet their parents do not see it.

This is important, because parents tend to underestimate the stresses experienced by their tweens and teens to about the same degree as they under-report their teens' risky behavior, including drug use and sexual activity. Parents also underestimate depression in their children. Past and current studies have found that parents can be a strong influence on their children's odds of drinking and shed light on how the influence plays out among adolescents (23). 28

Other research shows that a close parent-child relationship, one in which teenagers can turn to parents to discuss their feelings, delays the age of first intoxication. "Lack of attunement," a parent not knowing how their child is feeling or what their child is doing, is a significant disruption to healthy emotional and social development. Teens that have not been attuned to do not develop the necessary skills to manage their emotions, to control their behaviors, to negotiate relationships, to handle stress, to ask for help. These are major factors in teens turning to intoxication and the pseudo-social world of users as a resource to feel better.

However, when kids are attuned to, they experience the reassuring feeling that "my parents get me." Adolescent experimentation then is grounded in the safe, reassuring relationship with the parents. An attuned relationship is encouraging, tolerant, and limiting, all of which provides a supportive safety net for youth to explore but feel supported and contained.

Parents own use of substances is an important factor in teen substance abuse. As shown earlier, the drinking habit of parents has an influence on their children in both direct and indirect ways. An intoxicated parent cannot be an attuned parent, and as such, gives a child a double dose of risks by modeling addictive behavior and by not providing an emotional safety net.

Co-morbid psychiatric disorders significantly increase a teen's vulnerability to substance dependence. Depression, anxiety disorders, early childhood trauma, attention-deficit disorder, learning disabilities and school failure often lead to seeking substances as a source of relief, escape, and a way to fit in.

Substance abuse is a bad illness that can happen to good kids and well-meaning families. Clinicians specializing in the treatment of young people with addictive disorders see many wonderfully bright, talented, sensitive, ambitious kids who through a convergence of risk factors have developed a serious drug problem. The consequences permeate all areas of their lives: family, friends, school, money, sports, physical and mental health, and so forth. In addition, some otherwise law abiding young people have their first brush with the legal system because of their drug use.

Notes: Chapter 1

1. Giedd, J.N., et al. 1996. Quantitative magnetic resonance imaging of human brain development ages 4-18. *Cereb. Cortex* 6:551- 560.

2. Pefeferbaum, A., et al. 1994. A quantitative magnetic resonance imaging study of changes in the brain morphology from infancy to late adulthood. *Arch. Neurol.* 51:874-887.

3. Spear, L.P. 2000. The adolescent brain and age-related behavioral manifestations. *Neurosci. Biobev. Rev* 24: 417-463.

4. Yurgelun-Todd, D. et al. 2002. Sex differences in cerebral tissue volume and cognitive performance during adolescence. *Psych. Rep.* 91: 743-757.

5. Clark, C. *Hurt: Inside the World of Today's Teenagers.* (Baker Book House 2005).

6. Donald, M., *A mind so rare: The evolution of human consciousness.* (New York, Norton 2001) and Giedd, J. N. (1999). "Development of the human corpus callosum during childhood and adolescence: A longitudinal MRI study." *Progress in Neuro-Psychopharmacology & Biological Psychiatry* 23: 571-588.

7. Giedd, J. N., J. Blumenthal, et al. (1999). "Brain development during childhood and adolescence: A longitudinal MRI study." *Nature Neuroscience* 2(10): 861-863.

8. Office of Applied Studies. (2005). Results from the 2004 National Survey on Drug Use and Health: National findings (DHHS Publication No. SMA 05-4062, NSDUH

Series H-28). Rockville, MD: Substance Abuse and Mental Health Services Administration.

9. Schore, A.N. *Affect Dysregulation and Disorders of the Self.* (New York: W.W. Norton, 2003).

10. Siegel, D. J. *The Developing Mind* (The Guilford Press, 1999).

11. Panksepp, J. *Affective neuroscience: the foundations of human and animal emotions.* (Oxford University Press, 2004).

12. Schore, A. N. *Affect Dysregulation and Disorders of the Self.* (New York, W.W. Norton, 2003).

13. Siegel, D. J. *The Developing Mind* (The Guilford Press, 1999).

14. Johnston, L. D., O'Malley, P. M., Bachman, J. G., & Schulenberg, J. E. (2009). Monitoring the Future national results on adolescent drug use: Overview of key findings, 2008 (NIH Publication No. 09-7401). Bethesda, MD: National Institute on Drug Abuse.

15. Testimony by Charles Curie, M.A., A.C.S.W, April 26, 2005. Substance Abuse and Mental Health Service Administration U.S. Department of Health and Human Services on Substance Abuse Prevention Programs of the Substance Abuse and Mental Health Services Administration before Subcommittee on Criminal Justice, Drug Policy and Human Resources Committee on Government Reform United States House of Representatives http://www.hhs.gov/asl/testify/t050427.html.

16. Califano, Joseph. A., Jr. *High Society: How Substance Abuse Ravages America and What to Do About It* (Public Affairs, New York, 2007).

17. Grant BF, Dawson DA (1998): Age of onset of drug use and its association with DSM-IV drug abuse and dependence: Results from the National Longitudinal Alcohol Epidemiologic Survey. *J Subst Abuse* 10:163-173.

18. University of Mississippi Marijuana Potency Monitoring Project, Report 95, Jan 9 2007; http://www.ondcp.gov/dfc/files/marijuana_potency.pdf.

19. J.C. Merrill, K. Fox, S.R. Lewis, and G.E. Pulver, Cigarettes, Alcohol, Marijuana: Gateways to Illicit Drug Use (New York, N.Y.: Center on Addiction and Substance Abuse at Columbia University, 1994).

20. The Schneider Institute for Health Policy, Brandeis University for the Robert Wood Johnson Foundation, Princeton, New Jersey. Substance Abuse: The Nation's Number One Health Problem. Key Indicators for Policy (update) Feb. 2001.

21. Substance Abuse and Mental Health Services Administration, Office of Applied Studies. Drug Abuse Warning Network, 2006: National Estimates of Drug-Related Emergency Department Visits. DAWN Series D-30, DHHS Publication No. (SMA) 08-4339, Rockville, MD 2008).

22. Dorothy P. Rice, Sander Kelman, Leonard S. Miller, and Sarah Dunmeyer. The Economic Costs of Alcohol and Drug Abuse and Mental Illness: 1985, report submitted to the Office of Financing and Coverage Policy of the Alcohol, Drug Abuse, and Mental Health Administration (San Francisco, Calif.: Institute for Health & Aging,

University of California, U.S. Department of Health and Human Services, 1990).

23. J.C. Merrill, K. Fox, S.R. Lewis, and G.E. Pulver, Cigarettes, Alcohol, Marijuana: Gateways to Illicit Drug Use, (New York, N.Y.: Center on Addiction and Substance Abuse at Columbia University, 1994).

24. Alcoholism: Clinical & Experimental Research. Parental Drinking and Parenting Practices Influence Adolescent Drinking. *ScienceDaily* 4 February 2008. 11 June 2009 http://www.sciencedaily.com /releases/2008/02/080203174447.htm.

25. The Partnership Attitude Tracking Survey (PATS). Teens 2007 Report; Released August 4, 2008; www.drugfree.org/Files/full_report_teens_2008.

26. Schore, A.N. *Affect Dysregulation and Disorders of the Self.* (New York: W.W. Norton, 2003).

27. Belkin, Lisa: http://parenting.blogs.nytimes.com/2009/11/05/helping-our-children-with-stress/11-05, 2009, 12:46 pm.

28. Blos, P. in *The Fragile Alliance: An Orientation to Psychotherapy of the Adolescent*, J. Meeks, W. Bennett (Krieger Pub Co; 5th ed., 2001).

Chapter 2

A Young Adult Crisis

D is 21 years old, well muscled, and has a bit of facial stubble. He lounges on the couch in a T-shirt, shorts and flip-flops. At age 18, D fell apart during his freshman year in college. Having come from a highly controlling family, he said, "College was like being let out of jail," and he began drinking and smoking marijuana to excess. His peers nicknamed him Dooby D and Crunk [a reference to being a crazy drunk]. *He didn't attend many classes and failed all but one his first semester. At semester break he hit a light pole while driving intoxicated. He was arrested and his parents sent him to an upscale rehabilitation center for 60 days. After a number of treatment failures he is living at home, is in ongoing counseling, and working part-time for his father. He's angry with his father because D believes he reneged on their work agreement. Instead of a weekly allowance, D's father agreed to pay him $15 per hour for 10 hours of work each week, but had judged the quality of D's work as inadequate, so didn't pay him for some of the hours worked. D also is upset because his girlfriend is disappointed that he does not have a real job.*

Young adulthood is generally thought of as the period from ages 18 to 25. Although not closely examined by most developmental theorists, the period of transition from childhood and adolescent dependence to young adulthood and adult independence is fraught with vulnerability. Most parents understand it to be a fragile transition period. Parents worry if their children can effectively set goals and work toward them. They wonder if their children can cope with disappointments and demonstrate resilience, and finally, they worry about their children's ability to achieve independence.

Likewise, many young adults in treatment talk about feeling pessimistic and gloomy about the future. Many tether their feelings to the economy; when asked, others believe they will have difficulty being as financially well off as their parents. Many young people in our program also say that the government is inadequate to address major problems like the economy and environmental issues. Young adults express concerns, bordering on pessimism, about finding a job, finding a mate, raising a family, and having financial security. Various media reports echo these sentiments.

It is in this anxiety filled struggle to make commitments in the face of uncertainty, where substance abuse and addiction can easily insinuate itself into young adults' lives. When a young person feels too inadequate and overwhelmed to navigate the challenge of commitment, then they drift toward substance abuse as a means of self-soothing. In doing so, they experience a false sense of socialization and occupation; using substances is simply something to do.

D just had his 21st birthday. He is doing well in his recovery, but feels lonely and bored. "I feel like going back to using. At least I had something to do every day and people to hang out with, even if they weren't real friends."

It is this kind of terrifying "tipping point" that defines the young adult struggle. On a nearly daily basis, therapists and parents who are helping young people to abstain from drugs and navigate their lives must confront this simultaneous conundrum of vulnerability and promise.

Prevalence of Use

A 2004 SAMSHA (Substance Abuse and Mental Health Services Administration) news release states, "Historically, young adults have the highest rates of substance abuse." As mentioned in chapter one, adult substance abuse, particularly persistent and self-destructive abuse often begins in adolescence. The earlier in adolescence it begins, the higher the risk that it will persist into a disabling disorder in adulthood. But young adulthood has its own set of challenges. Young adulthood has evolved into a kind of "time out" period, a sort of "wink and a nod" to the idea that this is the time to explore and enjoy, particularly in the college environment.

We can note that although young adults are widely acknowledged to comprise the highest age group for substance abuse, they appear to be the least studied. It is as if there is a collective denial, or looking the other way for young people in this age group. This is helpful in the sense that it allows young adults to experiment and explore with relative security before they have to make a life commitment. But for a significant percentage of young adults, this is a period filled with unmanageable uncertainty and insecurity. It is often the first time they are away from home and on their own, and at this age one illusion of independence is the opportunity to try illicit substances for the first time. Or for many who have experimented with substances in adolescence, the freedom and lack of restraint during young adulthood gives them the opportunity to fully indulge, which might mean their use develops into abuse and dependence. Only 7% of teens meet criteria for substance abuse or dependency. That number triples in young adulthood, with 21% meeting criteria. This should shake the rest of us out of any complacency. One in five individuals between the ages of 18-25 with a serious drug and alcohol problem amounts to a national crisis.

Alcohol abuse is common in the young adult age group. Only 30% of high school students report recreational alcohol abuse and 17% report regular binge drinking. Those numbers nearly double in the 18-20 year old group to 49.7% regular users and 34.7 binge users. Then, among those ages 21-25, regular use rises to 70.2% and a frightening 46.5% who report regular binges.

Remember that binge drinking is significantly more dangerous and intractable than even regular heavy use. Binge drinkers tend to get much more intoxicated and impaired than regular users, putting them at greater risk for alcohol-related incidents like alcohol poisoning, motor vehicle accidents, injuries from falling, violence, sexual assault, and so forth. Because they have periods in which they do not drink, binge drinkers often make stronger arguments that their drinking is under their control. These individuals tend to be more steeped in denial than other types of drinkers and they are more resistant to treatment.

Alcohol use in particular seems to be a rite of passage in college where those enrolled report nearly twice as much alcohol consumption as those not attending college. And most drinking in college is binge drinking, with 44% of college students reporting binge drinking at least once per week, but many report drinking to intoxication two to three times per week. Students who are frequent binge drinkers are 20 times more likely to miss class, not complete assignments, go on academic probation, vandalize school property, engage in violent confrontations, and be involved with campus police.

Cigarette smoking rises dramatically in this age group; 45.6% report regular tobacco use, again double that of the teen years. Tobacco use is correlated to higher substance abuse. Young people who do not attend college or are part-time students use tobacco and illicit drugs significantly more than fulltime college students. However, fulltime college students have a notably higher rate of alcohol abuse. Being a fulltime college student and in particular, graduating from college, decreases the likelihood of tobacco use and substance dependence. On the other hand, dropping out and not completing college is a strong predictor of later substance dependence.

Working fulltime decreases tobacco and alcohol consumption; even working part-time provides some protection. So, breaking these trends down, unemployed youth, who are not in college, are at highest risk for tobacco, alcohol, and illicit substance abuse. Minorities are over represented in the nonstudent/unemployed group, with the exception of those of Asian descent, who have a lower rate of substance use of all kinds.

Rural youth have higher rates of alcohol and methamphetamine dependence than their urban cohorts. Native Americans, who are minorities and rural, have the highest rates of unemployment and substance abuse during young adulthood.

Young adults who smoke cigarettes are twice as likely to regularly use alcohol, marijuana, and other substances like cocaine and heroin. Nicotine is particularly insidious, and youths who smoke tobacco are much more likely to report symptoms of dependence: they try to quit, but fail; they have physiologic cravings and withdrawal symptoms; and persist in using tobacco despite negative consequences they would like to avoid. Nicotine is an easily accessible gateway into the experience of a mind-altering substance that leads to the loss of control and helplessness that we call dependence. (1)

Accessibility is a strong contributor to young adult substance use. Alcohol and marijuana have become easily accessible; 50% of young adults say that it is fairly easy or very easy to obtain alcohol. In addition, a whopping 78% of young adults said they knew of prescription medications or over-the-counter medications that they could obtain for the purposes of getting intoxicated.

Data from the 2003 NSDUH (National Survey on Drug Use and Health) indicate that 4.0 percent of youth ages 12 to 17 reported nonmedical use of prescription medications in the past month. But rates of abuse were highest among the 18-25 age group (6.0 percent), with opioid narcotics, sedatives, and prescription stimulants like Ritalin being the most common. Young women are slightly more likely than young men to use prescription medications for nonmedical purposes. (2)

Young adults often justify their abuse of prescription medications by claiming to use the medication for the intended purpose:

- *I twisted my ankle so I took Vicodin from my parents' cabinet for the pain.*
- *I was stressed and couldn't sleep so I took a Xanax my friend gave me.*
- *I had a big test and was tired so I took some Ritalin I had left over from when I was a kid.*

Although much of this kind of self-prescribing goes on, more often the medicines are being swallowed, snorted, and mixed for the purpose of getting intoxicated.

Among young adults, 16.4% report marijuana abuse and about the same number use marijuana whether they attend college or not. Unemployment is a strong predictor of higher marijuana use among young adults. About 2% of young adults report cocaine and methamphetamine abuse. Another 2.5% report using heroin and other narcotics. Again, youth not attending college and who are unemployed are at highest risk for regular use of illicit substances. Those youth who do not graduate from high school have the highest tobacco, alcohol, and illicit substance use.

Almost 70% of high school graduates attend college for some period of time during young adulthood. Amazingly, only 17% complete a four year degree by age 25. Those who drop out actually have a higher risk for substance abuse than those who never attended college in the first place. In a population of 32 million youth, most of whom are employed part-time or unemployed and not enrolled in college, the natural predilection is toward substance abuse. About 6 million individuals ages 18-25 meet criteria for substance abuse or dependence. (3)

Contributing Variables

D's dad had been an alcoholic and a workaholic just as his father had been. After D's mother left when D was five years old, his dad quit drinking and was determined not to allow D to follow the same path. He set up a strict schedule of school and structured recreation for D. D excelled at both. He was an excellent student and an outstanding soccer and basketball player until he reached high school, at which point he felt tired and didn't enjoy sports. The friends he had from sports were busy so he spent time alone at home, studying and maintaining a high grade point average because he knew that was his dad's biggest concern. Though his father didn't know about it, in tenth grade he started occasionally smoking marijuana with a neighborhood acquaintance. D had symptoms of depression in high school, including poor sleep, low energy, and lack of interest in activities previously enjoyed. He had passing thoughts of suicide, but never voiced them to his father or to anyone else. He often fantasized about how much fun college was going to be. His dad also supported the notion that college would be the best time in D's life.

Cultural Attitudes Matter, Too

As discussed above, many issues contribute to young adult substance abuse. Perhaps the strongest contributing factor is the cultural attitude toward the use of substances during this phase of life. In select cultures, attitudes greatly influence the development of alcohol use and abuse. For example, we can look at Italians and Italian American families, French and French American families, and Jewish families in Israel and America. These population groups tend to consume more alcohol than the average American family, but have lower incidences of alcoholism and alcohol-related social, psychological, medical, and legal problems.

Irish and Irish American families and Protestant families here and abroad have very different profiles. Though consumption is high in Irish families, attitudes toward drinking are negative and there is a high degree of alcoholism and alcohol related problems. Protestant families consume alcohol at lower than average rates, but have intensely ambivalent attitudes toward alcohol, and experience a higher incidence of alcohol addiction and alcohol related problems.

We can see these cultural generalities in individual families and in cultures. Youth from families with relaxed values towards social drinking, but strong prohibitions towards intoxication, have lower rates of alcohol dependence. Youth from "dry counties" in various regions of the country have a less than average rate of alcohol consumption, but a higher per capita rate of alcohol related problems. Consistency in stated values and practice seem to be important factors in developing healthy attitudes towards alcohol use.

The majority of parents say they have no control over their young adults' use of substances. The prevailing attitude is that once young people celebrate their eighteenth birthday, they must make their own decisions about drug and alcohol use. Yet those ages 18 or older who reported losing privileges, such as a car, a phone, or their allowance, because of substance abuse were less likely to develop substance dependence. Youth whose parents clearly express disapproval of marijuana use were significantly less likely to develop substance abuse of any kind.

Conversely, parents who do not talk to their teens and young adults about alcohol and drug abuse, and who do not follow through with limits and consequences about the use of substances, find that their children have a higher incidence of substance abuse related problems.

Young adults who report using drugs and alcohol for recreational purposes are significantly less likely to develop substance dependence than those who report using these substances to cope with stress. Young adults face many stresses. School failure and unemployment are listed as highly stressful and are strongly correlated with substance abuse, particularly among males. Females rank troubled relationships as highly as academic, occupational, and financial stresses.

Most in the 18-25 age group are still deeply concerned about their relationships with their families. Divorce, family illness, financial problems, and parent-child conflicts are listed as serious stresses that contribute to misuse of substances. Low socioeconomic status is strongly correlated with substance abuse and substance dependence. Young adults from families below the poverty line are nearly three times more likely to have substance abuse disorders.

Psychiatric problems among young adults also are highly correlated with substance abuse. Interestingly, psychiatric problems like depression, bipolar disorder, schizophrenia, panic disorder, obsessive compulsive disorder, and eating disorders often are first present in adolescence but for most youth, the full blown syndromes do not appear until young adulthood. Those who drop out of or never attend college have only marginally higher rates of psychiatric disorders. The exception is that those who do not attend college, particularly those that did not complete high school, have significantly higher incidences of personality disorders. Personality disorders are highly correlated with substance abuse and dependence.

Many young people begin losing control of substance use because of insomnia, an early symptom in many psychiatric disorders like depression, anxiety, and bipolar disorder. Young adults often use the effects of substances to counter unpleasant symptoms: stimulants to fight depression, alcohol and narcotics to counter anxiety or over-excitability, or marijuana to help with sleep and poor anger control.

We hear ongoing debates about the genetic component of substance abuse. Certainly, strong evidence suggests that both alcohol and substance abuse disorders are, at least in part, influenced by general genetic factors. Family studies and twin studies suggest that the common genetic factors seem to be most closely related to disruptions in stress management systems, particularly in the hypothalamic-pituitary-adrenal (HPA) axis. This common genetic liability has also been connected to risks for mood and anxiety disorders and for disinhibited behavior associated with certain types of personality disorders, like antisocial and narcissistic personality disorders.

Other genetic factors appear to be more specific, however. In recent years, researchers have identified genes influencing risk for alcohol dependence. These genes are involved in alcohol metabolism and affected individuals have high alcohol tolerance, which leads to excessive alcohol intake to achieve intoxication. In addition, other genes have been discovered that influence the transmission of nerve cell signals and modulation of nerve cell activity in different neurochemical systems that are implicated in substance abuse. Some genes influence the GABA system, which can be connected to alcohol and sedative abuse; genes that alter the endogenous opioid system can be linked to opioid narcotic dependence, and genes that control natural cannabinoids that are linked to marijuana abuse.

None of these findings are definitive in establishing specific genetic connections to substance abuse and dependency.

Substance abuse does not have a single line of traceable causality. Rather, substance abuse is a multi-factorial problem, like a giant puzzle with many pieces. Understanding substance abuse requires looking at all of these pieces and how they interact with each other.

The Best Time of Life. Really?

As mentioned above, many young adults are less optimistic about their future prospects than previous generations. They expect to earn less money and have a lower standard of living than their parents. They report less faith in marriage as a lifelong commitment and anticipate having both more than one career and more than one life partner. Many youth express pessimism about obtaining a well-paying job or being successful professionally. They report worries about finding a satisfactory life partner. They express mistrust and lack of confidence in government and leaders to solve problems like unemployment, economic decline, rising illiteracy, growing income disparity, deteriorating environment, and so forth. When asked if their pessimism might cause them to abuse substances more, a significant number report "just wanting some excitement," or "it doesn't matter either way."

Despite a general attitude of young adulthood being the "best time in life," the more obvious truth is that like all stages of development, young adulthood is filled with opportunities and perils. Young adults are stressed, just as many teens and adults are stressed. Those ages 18-25 struggle with relationships, economic worries, family problems, psychiatric symptoms, and genetic vulnerabilities; they also have deep fears of failing and of disappointing themselves and the people they care about. These stresses and many other factors make them vulnerable to misuse intoxicating substances to feel better, and then vulnerable to the loss of control over substances to the point of abuse or dependency. Our cultural "blind eye" towards this age group amounts to denial of their vulnerability and contributes to their loss of control.

Consequences

In rehab D learned about oxycontin and as soon as he got out and returned home he started using it regularly. Later, D went to a 30 day detox center, then to a halfway house for six months. He became very depressed there and had a serious suicide attempt. He was hospitalized and then returned home to live with his dad and stepmom. Due to unmanageable conflict, they moved him into an apartment with a friend. He resumed use of marijuana and oxycontin. He and his friend were arrested for stealing copper wire from a local warehouse.

On any given day, far too many young people are using alcohol and other substances to become intoxicated. Intoxication disrupts control of emotion, impairs information gathering, and undermines both problem solving and decision making. Intoxicants often lead to sensory distortion, altered perception, and poor motor coordination. The consequences of this activity range from benign to catastrophic. Many use substances recreationally and experience mild negative consequences like nausea and vomiting, bumps and bruises, mild damage to property, or brief disruptions of social, academic, or occupational functioning. The regularity of these mild consequences contributes to distortion of the risks, and to denial.

Serious consequences occur daily, almost hourly. Every year, nearly 400,000 young people report having unprotected sex while intoxicated; a quarter of those report being so intoxicated that they do not know if they even consented to sex. In addition, about 100,000 young women per year report being raped while intoxicated; many clearly remember not only saying no to sex, but saying no to further ingestion of intoxicants and the intoxicants being forced upon them.

Youth are injured, involved in fights, have legal problems, fail in school, lose friends, even disconnect from their families due to substance abuse. All of these disruptions seriously affect the challenge of young adulthood, accepting one's strengths and weaknesses and then making commitments based upon to what path those strengths and weaknesses are likely to lead.

Costs to Society of the Lack of Effective Treatment

D was diverted from the criminal justice system into an intensive outpatient program where he saw a psychiatrist and was placed on Buprenorphine for opiate dependence and a helpful antidepressant. He sees a counselor weekly, attends NA meetings three days per week, has a probation officer and weekly urine testing, and sees a separate counselor with his father twice per month. He struggles to keep a job and make friends who influence his life in a positive way. He does not feel prepared to return to school fulltime or even to take one class. His recovery is fragile, but slowly progressing.

Drug abuse and addiction are costly for individuals and for society. Economists estimate yearly tolls of $181 billion for illicit drugs, $193 billion for tobacco, and $235 billion for alcohol. Estimates of the total overall costs of substance abuse in the United States exceed $600 billion annually. Included in these costs are lost productivity. For example, workers ages 18-25 miss the most work days, sustain the most injuries, and make the most mistakes as a result of drug and alcohol related problems. These problems are in contrast to the fact young adults are generally healthy, unless they have significant drug and alcohol problems. At that point, young people have high health costs due primarily to injuries suffered in motor vehicle or other accidents.

Youth ages 18-25 are also over represented in the criminal justice system; 83% arrested have drug and alcohol problems. As surprising as these numbers may be, they do not fully describe the breadth of destructive public health and safety implications of drug abuse and addiction, such as family disintegration, loss of employment, failure in school, and lifelong disability. (4) A 2008 study in Massachusetts found 21% of transition age youth, 18-25, met criteria for a substance use disorder. This amounts to just over six million young adults nationwide. No clear data exist on the percentage of costs that this age group contributes to the annual national total cost of substance abuse, the $600 billion mentioned earlier. However, some estimate that young adults account for nearly one quarter of the total yearly substance abuse costs to the nation, close to 150 billion dollars. (5)

Like D, many young adults have a high rate of use, often of multiple substances. D estimated he spent over $40,000 on oxycontin alone in less than six months. Showing the recklessness that so many young adults have to a high degree, D drove his car into a light pole while drunk. The damage to his car, the pole, and his medical and legal costs totaled well over $30,000. Legal costs for stealing copper wire, including attorney fees, court costs, probation supervision, and restitution added up to over $25,000.

We also need to consider that D's treatment costs grew to over $150,000 because of prolonged stays at two expensive rehabilitation facilities, a psychiatric hospitalization, and continuing costs of outpatient treatment. In addition, D's insurance covered very little of his substance abuse and psychiatric costs. Since he has not been able to work or return to school, it is difficult to estimate the costs of D's loss of productivity. Although he dropped out of a college that costs $50,000 per year, his father pays his treatment, his rent, and a weekly allowance to cover monthly expenses. D does a small amount of weekly work in his dad's office and on their property.

D's case is typical. Many young adults have less severe and less costly problems, but many have much more severe and even costlier problems. D is still only 21. At the current rate, if his recovery derails, his costs will more than double by age 25. But these are the recognizable costs. There are severe social and emotional costs. D's relationship with his father and stepmother is battered with betrayal and misunderstanding. D has few friends outside of recovery. His confidence, self-esteem, and sense of self-efficacy, critical achievements during young adulthood, are seriously damaged. Realistically, his recovery will require another three to four years of treatment. It is likely that he will not finish his education until about age 30, if at all. He is at significant risk to have lifelong substance abuse and psychiatric problems that severely limit his emotional, social, and occupational functioning.

Even given D's circumstance, he is still among the more fortunate young adults with serious addictions. His family is wealthy and has been able to afford some of the best, most expensive treatment programs in the country. Sadly, few treatment programs are specifically targeted for young adults. Young adults are referred for substance abuse treatment three times more often than adolescents; however, programs specific to adolescents outnumber 30 to 1 those programs specific to young adults. For treatment purposes, young adults generally are considered adults and are admitted into programs with other adults ranging from ages 18 to 65. Young adults have the legal status of adults, and are referred to the adult criminal justice system where they retain all of the legal rights of adults, despite having little capacity to exercise those rights responsibly. Privacy issues in the legal system and in treatment are often serious obstacles for parents, youth, and for legal and health care professionals.

Only in the last few years have federal, state, and local authorities focused on the special needs of the young adult population. Much of this has been driven by the foster care system, where youth have tended to be abandoned at age 18, at which point many fall through the cracks. In addition, brain research has demonstrated that in young adulthood substantial brain growth continues, with the frontal lobes still maturing as late as age 22-25. These realizations have spurred rethinking of social and legal services, along with medical and mental health services targeted at this population.

Unfortunately, the recent decline in the economy has undermined efforts to continue to create and implement policies and programs for transition age youth. So again, these young adults are lumped in with adults, even though they represent a much more vulnerable and treatable group than adults over the age of 25 and even youth under the age of 15.

In spite of strained resources, we see a growing recognition of the special needs and opportunities for young adults. A nationwide survey of college professors revealed serious concerns about students' alcohol consumption. Higher rates of alcohol use is associated with more vandalism and property damage, more violence and sexual assaults, more injuries and medical problems, and lower academic performance. Currently, nearly all colleges have created alcohol counseling programs and four out of five campuses have alcohol-free residential options. A growing number of treatment programs around the country are creating separate categories for adolescents, young adults, and adults (over age 26).

Even with progress made, we still see a lack of understanding of the developmental needs of young adults; in addition, informed, effective treatment programs remain more of a goal than a reality. A 2003 study demonstrated that probationers ages 18-25 who enrolled in an outpatient drug rehabilitation program had significantly worse outcomes than older adults. The researchers noted that young adults had less capacity for self-reflection and were less able to take personal responsibility for their recovery than adults over age 25. Other researchers have noted that young adults have a higher incidence of psychiatric problems than adults over age 26.

Transition age youth also have more unstable relationships with family, friends, and romantic partners, and are more mistrustful of treatment professionals than older adults. They experience more conflicts about money and control because their parents or someone else is often paying for their participation in treatment. All of these issues indicate the need for more specialization to be successful with young adults. (6)

D and his parents are not alone. Every year, the six million young adults with serious substance abuse problems account for enormous costs in money, in injured or lost lives, and in the less measurable qualities of grief and despair. Understanding their unique vulnerabilities and strengths and targeting prevention and treatment specifically at this age group has become a national imperative.

Chapter 2 Notes

1.http://www.cdc.gov/mmwr/preview/mmwrhtml/mm6005a2.htm

2. 2003 NSDUH (National Survey on Drug Use and Health http://www.samhsa.gov/data/NSDUH.aspx).

3. http://measuringup.highereducation.org/_docs/2006/National Report_2006.pdf

4. http://www.justice.gov/ndic/pubs11/18862/impact.htm.

5. http://www.ncdhhs.gov/mhddsas/providers/CABHA/Training/ CHILDtraining-supplemental3.pdf

6. http://www.ncbi.nlm.nih.gov/pubmed/14510042.

Chapter 3
Family, Community and Culture

"If a community values its children it must cherish their parents"
John Bowlby (1)

All societies create expectations of individuals and families, but each person experiences societal pressures in different ways, some obvious and some more subtle. For example, the United States is characterized by undeniably positive features. As every schoolchild learns, this is the land of life, liberty, and the pursuit of happiness. Those principles have also made us the land of opportunity, creativity, individuality, equality, choice, and free speech. These attributes, desirable and prized across the world, have influenced our culture in positive ways; however, most of us recognize a downside, too. For example, the pressure to "keep up with the Jones' " has evolved to excessive concern with outward signs of affluence. U.S. culture also focuses on problem solving, achievement, and competition; we value individual autonomy, possibly so much that most of us fear dependence.

Our culture matches the left-brain dominant Type-A personality, the go-getters who strive to achieve and succeed. Moreover, we have added a near obsession with self-indulgence and self-image, which has promoted cosmetic surgery and other nonsurgical cosmetic procedures as valuable and even viable for almost everyone. Bariatric surgery, which encompasses both health and appearance, is now one of the fastest growing procedures in medicine.

Our culture encourages individuals to project idealized physical and personality images, and tools are available to facilitate certain kinds of change. For example, cosmetic surgery can change a nose or erase a wrinkle, and now, through chemicals, we can cosmetically alter the personality. Those diagnosed with a condition called "social anxiety" might be given a medication to treat it. We routinely use medications to alter the ability of a child to concentrate or conform to expected classroom behavior. Adults might use medications that influence them to go beyond natural tendencies and become more outgoing, assertive, energetic, and productive. While the use of these medications is linked with a specific diagnosis, one of the unintended results is a new type of conformity of behavior, but also of feelings and self-perception.

Our culture has defined certain norms we find desirable. For example, in terms of stereotyping the sexes, we do not "allow" men to be depressed or women to be angry, although the ways we diagnose depression and personality disorders among adults is changing. However, we see certain trends in the way we approach the development of young children and have created another norm.

For example, we increasingly see that preschool children are not allowed to just be kids who play and develop imagination and wonder—what we used to think of as the magic of childhood. Only a few decades ago, fulltime preschools and large-scale daycare centers were rare. Since so many women worked in the war effort during World War II, the manufacturing companies provided daycare in order to entice women to seek a job. Once the war ended, corporate daycare ended as well, not to make another appearance for two or three decades. The pendulum reverted back to the era when women were encouraged—even pressured—to stay home with children. Those who had to work hired a babysitter. Those preschoolers who attended nursery school at all usually participated for two or three mornings or afternoons a week, and these mini-playschools offered a chance to paint or play house and listen to stories. Until recently, daycare and preschool environments were not about "achievement" and learning specific skills as part of a preschool "curriculum."

Overall, we live in a pressurized culture, in that we are encouraged to push hard, do more, learn more, and achieve. Our society is famous for its emphasis on competition with each other and the rest of the world, and this has filtered down to our smallest members. Yesterday's kindergarteners learned shapes, colors, letters, and numbers in their half-day school, but in some school districts today, kindergarteners are expected to come to school with these basics mastered. Given the emphasis on accelerated learning, it is easy to see why parents are concerned with their children's ability to keep up with these early academic pressures.

Many within our culture internalize the pressure and push themselves in these directions. Unfortunately, a culture of striving can undermine relationships in that it does not allow for people to slow down and "be with" their child, spouse, friends, and neighbors.

Since achievement and autonomy go together in our culture, it follows that parents would become afraid their children will remain dependent and not achieve autonomy. Unfortunately, this fear has played itself out in many areas. For example, some parents fear breastfeeding for "too long," however that is defined, or co-sleeping, or holding babies too soon when they are distressed, and so forth. Pushing for autonomy tends to lead to devaluing attachment and the merger process between mother and child. This becomes part of the cultural norm to the extent

73

that some label it "normative abuse" (2). For example, Wallant argues that when parents give up their basic biological parenting instincts to acquiesce to current cultural norms, then these parents are participating in normative abuse. She says:

What a price we have paid for our fear of attachment. Perhaps, if the baby were protected by nursing, co-sleeping, and other forms of attachment parenting, he would be less predisposed to addiction in his teen and adult years. Although addiction is multidetermined, our goal should be to remove as many variables as possible so as to lessen the likelihood of its occurrence (3).

Our society's long-standing denial and devaluation of merger phenomenon throughout the life cycle have actually increased the likelihood of personality disorders and addiction, precisely because autonomy and independence have been encouraged at the expense of attachment needs. These disorders which are so pervasive in our current world illustrate that beneath the veneer of self-reliance lies the core of powerlessness, alienation, and detachment. The push for individuation and self-determination in young children has greatly affected the acting out and repressed behavior of [adolescents and] adults we later see in our psychotherapy practices, patients who suffer from what has been termed the basic fault (Balint), the false self (Winnicott), or the empty core (Seinfeld) (4).

A fundamental fear among many parents today is that if they respond "too warmly" to dependency needs during their children's infant years, they will end up raising "cry babies" and overly dependent individuals. However, that is not the outcome the data suggest. In fact, research shows that when mothers promptly picked up and comforted crying infants, the babies cried less by the end of the first year (5). Additional research found that the children who received prompt response in their first year were more self-sufficient and better able to self-soothe in the second year, in contrast to infants encouraged in their first year to work through emotional distress on their own (6).

Independence, autonomy, and achievement are ambient values, meaning they are always present and embedded in the culture whether parents are aware of it or not. These values operate as norms and influence the ways parents interact with their children during all stages of life. During their children's infancy, parents might fear raising a child who is not self-sufficient; later, parents might be afraid that their children will not be competitive enough to enter the workforce and support themselves and a family one day. Parents' fears can lead to early problems. For example, today, some children are given homework in preschool, which can lead to anxiety and sleep problems. We are increasingly observing that at a very young age, children feel the pressure to learn and adapt to our information and technologically oriented society.

Since attending preschool is a twenty-first century rite of passage, we see the growing popularity of "academic" preschools that promise to prepare kids for the cutthroat world of kindergarten. But are these competitive, academic preschools a good idea? Not really, many experts say. "Research…shows that academic preschools offer children no long-term advantages academically, but make them more anxious," says Roberta Golinkoff, author of *Einstein Never Used Flash Cards: How Our Children Really Learn and Why They Need to Play More and Memorize Less.*

According to Martha E. Mock, assistant professor at the University of Rochester Warner School of Education, every preschool is different, but the best ones share common traits. She says, "Young children learn best through meaningful interaction with real materials and caring adults and their peers, not through the drilling of isolated skills" (7).

Researchers at the University of Michigan asked young children to kiss sweet test-strips, which tested their cortisol levels, a stress hormone secreted in saliva. They reported that 70 to 80% of the test subjects in daycare and preschool had rising levels of cortisol through the day, with toddlers experiencing the biggest increases. The researchers found, however, that it was not separation anxiety that caused the stress; instead, social relationships — the experiences kids had at daycare — were the cause. The study also found that children with secure attachments to their caregivers had stable cortisol levels even when they were upset, another reason to give your child's kindly sensitive caregiver a great big hug (8).

"Keeping up with the Jones'," a euphemism for material success equal to neighbors—peers—has spilled over to workplace success and accomplishment. Most of us see it in our own lives and families, as well as in our communities. When I was a graduate student, my former wife was a new lawyer working in the private sector. Most of her work involved researching old cases, writing briefs, and filing legal documents. One evening she had a midnight deadline to deliver a legal filing in a drop box located a few miles from our apartment. She was clearly anxious, knowing that if she did not meet the filing deadline she would face consequences and repercussions the next day.

About 10:00 pm, we drove downtown to make the delivery. It was dark and the streets and sidewalks were empty. As we walked from the car to the drop-box, we saw a woman approaching the drop-box from another direction. Based on how fast she walked, I assumed she was trying to meet a legal filing deadline, too. She looked to be in her thirties or so, and had a briefcase in one hand and boy around age six in her other arm. The boy's head lightly bounced on her shoulder in rhythm to her purposeful gait. I was reminded of Betty Friedan's book *The*

Feminine Mystique, in which Friedan discussed women's struggle to have their careers and also raise their children.

Literally and figuratively, this woman had her profession in one hand and her dependent child in the other, and tried to make it all work. Not having children of my own at the time, I felt compassion for her and her child and wondered what it was like to have the simultaneous desire and need to do well on her job, provide financially for her family, and be a good parent too.

Clearly, it took effort to make it all work. I wondered if she had support from others in the family. Was no other person available at home to stay with her sleeping child? Could someone else—a friend or neighbor—have made the delivery? Why did she appear—at least in that moment—to lack the support every parent needs?

Just as children are absolutely dependent on their parents for sustenance, so in all but the most primitive communities, are parents, especially their mothers, dependent on a greater society for economic provision. If a community values its children it must cherish their parents (9).

Counselors and therapists routinely work with many intact two-parent families, in which both parents are highly educated and successful in their careers. Having wanted only the best for themselves and their children, they have achieved material signs of success. They live in the best neighborhoods with the best schools, and they can hire tutors if needed. They buy the best clothes, cars, sporting equipment, and so forth. With the best intentions, these parents have lived the societal script that tells them what is important—they have fallen for it hook, line, and sinker.

Many parents of "kids in trouble" put value on their balance sheets, accomplishments, status, and image, at least in part, because they believed it was up to them to provide the advantages that enable their children to compete and achieve, hence the "investment" in an academic preschool. However, often these parents are disconnected from their own need to balance rest, play, emotional support from others, and other internal experiences. They learned to disconnect from their internal world and, like the go-getters society values, they built lives that look good on the outside. They project an image that since all is abundant, all is well.

Consequently, parents who are split off from their own internal experiences and needs then tend to focus on their child's external conditions, often failing to recognize the child's internal needs and developing "self." Sadly, these parents fail to recognize their powerful role, and more specifically, their relationship with the emotional, psychological, and social development of their child.

In 2006, Levine published a book called *The Price of Privilege* (10), which cites the work of other researchers (11), who offer this concise picture of current developments in adolescent life: *America's newly identified at-risk group is preteens and teens from affluent, well-educated families. In spite of their economic and social advantages, they experience among the highest rates of depression, substance abuse, anxiety disorders, somatic complaints, and unhappiness of any group of children in this country.*

In my clinical practice, I see evidence of this external focus every day. For example, adolescents may engage in cutting or burning behaviors (self-mutilation) or they use drugs. Parents immediately become concerned, and on the surface their response looks good. In the moment, parents accept the reality of the external events and realize that their children are struggling and need help. However, I have noted that when teens come to my practice with a substance abuse or self-mutilation disorder, they have been at it for at least two years. In other words, these behaviors have been going on for a relatively long time, but the parents failed to see them. Generally, parents freely admit their lapse within the first 20 minutes of our first interview.

In addition, the teens I see who use drugs or cut or burn themselves have been struggling with depression for quite some time. The parents did not notice their child's internal struggle, going on for a year or two, or even longer, until obvious external signs appeared. Not only are these teens depressed and struggling, but they also experience "not being seen." They hurt inside, but no one notices; it is as if they were invisible. In this situation, teens become exhausted from using so much psychic energy to make sense of their pain and internally regulate it on their own. Since others do not see their pain and need for support, they conclude that no one is present to soothe them. In this situation, young people become emotionally and psychologically stuck, mistrustful of others' capacity to soothe them. These adolescents and young adults then often resort to self-destructive coping strategies such as turning inward, becoming avoidant. Many have insecure attachment, which results in their belief they cannot turn to others for help. This leads to an over-reliance on themselves, drugs, alcohol, and cutting/burning (more common among girls) to regulate their affective states.

To help adolescents and young adults become unstuck and heal, a significant part of the therapist's job involves helping parents become more informed about how to "see" and "be with" their child. A colleague of mine said, "Parents need to figure out how much they need to slow down... and then slow down a little bit more." This principle of slowing down is a prerequisite for parents as they work to understand and support their child. The idea of slowing down can be quite a jolt to parents who have spent many years striving to give themselves and their children what they thought was most important.

Dan Siegel, MD, says that children need to "feel felt." We know this occurs when children experience a sense of "you really

79

get me" with their parents. Feeling felt, connected to, and understood all validate internal experiences and allow children to develop emotionally, psychologically, and socially (12).

Devaluing relationships and over-valuing external material possessions, status, and achievements is a form of "misinformation" that prevails in our culture. It is what leads well-intentioned parents to miss what is important for themselves and their children. Unfortunately, when parents want to value emotional and psychological health and development, they encounter heavy and difficult pressures they must counter.

Marris (13), as cited by Bretherton (14), points to the fundamental tension between the desire to create a secure and predictable social order and the desire to maximize one's own opportunities at the expense of others. According to Marris, a good society is one which, as far as is humanly possible, minimizes disruptive events, protects each child's experience of attachment from harm, and supports family coping. Yet, in order to control uncertainty, individuals and families are tempted to achieve certainty at the expense of others (i.e., by imposing a greater burden of uncertainty on them or by providing fewer material and social resources). When powerful groups in society promote their own control over life circumstances by subordinating and marginalizing others, they make it less possible for these groups to offer and experience security in their own families. Valuing attachment and connection thus has public policy and moral implications for society, not just psychological implications for attachment dyads.

A Novel Idea

Bhutan is a country nestled in the Himalayas between India and China, and is now one of the fastest growing economies in the world. Although only recently interested in participating economically with the rest of the world, as evidenced by its

80

recent application to the World Trade Organization (WTO), the country's leaders still have not focused on their Gross Domestic Product (GDP), which the U.S. and most other countries use to measure economic performance. Instead, the Bhutanese chose to define a Gross National Happiness (GNH).

As Bhutan participates in the global economy, its citizens also want to make sure economic development will not undermine their cultural value of relationships and happiness. The Bhutanese recognize the risks of becoming connected to the global economy, thereby undermining hundreds of years of culture and values that existed in relative isolation—they were the last country in the world to allow television. As a relatively new representative democracy, the Bhutanese assert that GNH will help both leaders and citizens promote sustainable socio-economic development, preserve and promote cultural values, conserve the natural environment, and establish good governance.

The Bhutanese have received a great deal of attention for their GNH (15), because to most people in the majority of countries, it seems amazing that anyone would actually measure happiness, which covers the concepts of contentment and satisfaction with relationships.

When Thomas Jefferson wrote "The Declaration of Independence" he carefully chose the words "life, liberty and the pursuit of happiness" to indicate the value placed on the rights of the individual. However, these rights were never meant to imply that we should concern ourselves with material wellbeing alone. Our society has always valued personal accomplishment, independence, competition, free will, and freedom to pursue financial gain. When these values are out of balance, however, we see the results in the form of overstretched, unsupported parents who are stressed and burned out. Family life might feel like a list of chores to accomplish.

When a society does not support or see the value of attachment and relationships, it is difficult to be a consistent, warm, nurturing, and attuned parent, which is why parenthood often feels like "doing" tasks and chores rather than "being" a mother or father with a child.

Chapter 3: Notes

1. Bowlby, J. Maternal care and mental health. *World Health Organization Monograph* (Serial No. 2, p.84) 1951.

2. Wallant, Karen B. *Creating the Capacity for Attachment: Treating Addictions and the Alienated Self.* (Jason Aronson, 2002).

3. Wallant, K.B., p.xxi (2002).

4. Wallant, K.B., p. 2 (2002).

5. Ainsworth, M.D.S., Bell, S., & Stayton, D. Infant-Mother attachment and social development: Socialization as a product of reciprocal responsiveness to signals. In M. Richards (Ed.), *The Integration of the Child into the Social World* (pp.99-135). (Cambridge, UK: Cambridge University Press, 1974).

6. Sroufe, Egeland, Carlson & Collins. *The Development of the Person: The Minnesota Study of Risk and Adaptation from Birth to Adulthood.* (The Guilford Press, 2005).

7. Boyd, H. Academic Preschools: Too Much Too Soon? Topics: Early Years (Birth-5), Preschool, Summer, Academic Preschool, http://www.education.com/magazine/article/ Ed_Academic_Preschools/.

8. Parent Time Stress Taste Test for Preschoolers by Cathie Kryczka, http://www.todaysparent.com/lifeasparent/article. jsp?content=20060410_125308_5388&page=) originally published in *Today's Parent Baby & Toddler*, Spring 2006.

9. Bowlby, J. 1951.

10. Levine, Madeline. *The Price of Privilege* (HarperCollins, 2006).

11. Luthar, S. S., & Sexton, C. (2005). The high price of affluence. In R. V. Kail (Ed.), *Advances in Child Development*, 32, 126-162. San Diego, CA: Academic Press.

12. Siegel D. J. *The Developing Mind* (The Guilford Press, 1999).

13. Marris, P. The social construction of uncertainty. In Parkes, C.M, J., Stevenson-Hinde, J., Morris, P., (Eds.), *Attachment across the life* cycle (pp. 77- 90). (London: Routledge 2006).

14. Bretherton, I. The Origins of Attachment Theory: John Bowlby and Mary Ainsworth. *Developmental Psychology* (1992), *28*, 759-775.

15. http://www.chinapost.com.tw/asia/2008/11/08/182274/New-king.htm.

Chapter 4
The Stages of Drug Use and the Rapid Progression

 At age 17, Scott is a pleasant young man, but also anxious and hyper-vigilant. Having recently celebrated nine months of sobriety, he arrived at my office for his weekly session wearing a tattered "skater" shirt, his thin tan beanie, and his usual baggy pants. As far back as he could remember, Scott struggled to feel comfortable in his skin and talked often about his difficulty making friends, even in the first grade. His feelings of insecurity prevented him from reaching out and simply playing with his peers.

Over time, other kids had tuned into Scott's insecurity and social inadequacy, which then led them to pick on him and tease. Along with insecurities, Scott was sensitive to shame, but at the same time he longed to connect with other kids. At an early age, he became preoccupied with the needs and wants of others in an attempt to keep them close.

Scott's developmental history detailed the same relational dynamic. For example, he had never felt as adequate and lovable as his siblings, but he still longed for his parents approval. He had memories of being a very small child preoccupied with what it would take to be the gleam in his parents' eyes.

His parents were professionals, who worked long hours and were concerned with maintaining their external image as accomplished and affluent parents with an attractive, successful family. Throughout his childhood, Scott tried to be happy and sought to sense and meet his parents' needs. Because he did not want to burden his parents or appear weak, he did not share his hurt, sadness, and anger over internal or external conflicts and the troublesome events that affected his life. As a result, even before starting school, Scott felt insecure and lost. He was already exhausted from using so much mental energy to work through emotional issues on his own, not to mention the "song and dance act" he performed to find approval, acceptance, and love. By the time Scott reached junior high school he found drugs, which provided temporary psychological soothing, a new identity, and a culture comprised of individuals who took him in and accepted him for who he is—provided he had drugs to share.

During this particular counseling session, he seemed far more grounded than usual as he sat in silence and reflected on his history of drug use. He had only recently begun putting some pieces together about the way he experienced himself and his life prior to his drug addiction, including its progression over time. I had seen him finally reach a place in which he could make sense of the larger picture of his story, with its beginning, middle, and end. In addition, he had begun to connect to himself in a more emotional—visceral—way as he talked about his past. He had moved beyond the intellectual understanding that he had a problem with drugs and now struggled within to feel equal to others. In addition, learning to regulate his emotions meant he was "getting it" at a gut level.

Scott sat quietly on the couch for four minutes, the longest amount of time Scott had ever spent in a counseling session *silently* thinking about his experiences. When he finally looked up, his contemplative expression changed to reflect both a sense of wonder and an awakening, a sign he at last made sense of the totality of his history.

With an inflection in his voice that sounded like both a statement and a question, he said: *I think I see what happened to me… I feel tired and my stomach feels anxious thinking about saying it, but here goes. I never wanted to use drugs. I remember learning from my parents and teachers that drugs were*

86

dangerous. But watching other kids use drugs and desperately wanting to connect with them made me feel like I was supposed to use drugs, too. And drugs didn't seem to be a problem for the kids I saw using in junior high school. When my friends first offered drugs I remember feeling more afraid of not using them and then being disliked by the group, than being afraid of what drugs could do to my body or being punished for it by my parents. Given the choice of being unpopular with my friends or hurting my body and being punished by my parents, I would take physical injury and parental punishment any day. I had to belong...I just had to...and I hate that I felt like that.

I would chill out and watch them laughing and having fun, connecting and sharing their connective experience while they got wasted. I just sat there feeling like I was missing out. I was again on the outside looking in. I started to ask what it felt like to be high. They all said it was cool and that I should just try it. The next time we hung out, I decided to go along, and that was the first time I got high.

I remember laughing with the other kids, feeling connected, so before I knew it, I was asking them to pass me some more. Suddenly I was in. I finally felt like I belonged. It felt great, and using drugs didn't seem like a problem for me at the time. Shoot, I even began making lots of new friends and got invitations to all kinds of parties. I ended up with more friends and people wanting to hang out with me than I'd ever had before. I thought all of the internal struggles I felt over all those years in the past were now gone—I'd solved my problems.

The next thing I knew, I was getting wasted every weekend, and I was only 'chillin' out with more and more drug users. Damn, then I smoked pot before and after school, and I found myself pulling away from my family. Then I started lying to them to get more money to buy more pot and other drugs. That's when my life really went downhill fast.

Scott's narrative sheds light on how insecurity was a set up for him to fall into drug culture and addiction. Even in his earliest memories he was driven to fit in, which naturally led to an ongoing struggle to navigate peer relationships.

Many circumstances converged to leave Scott vulnerable to picking up drugs the first time and to continue to use until he became addicted. These same factors are common among millions of today's young people. Scott struggled with insecurity, along with underdeveloped brain chemistry, because of his young age, and underdeveloped affect regulation and social skills, mixed with the potency of today's drugs. Together, these factors, more often than not, form a situation that contributes to a rapid progression from first use to addiction for many teenagers. As relatively recent data suggest (discussed in chapter 1), the younger the age of first intoxication, the more likely it is that the individual will progress to addiction.

As mentioned earlier, more pages in the DSM IV (1) are dedicated to substance abuse disorders than to any other disorder. In addition, to accurately diagnose disorders in other categories, clinicians must first rule out substance abuse. Treating young people is already tricky enough. After all, they are going through physical and psychological changes, which tax the body-mind regulatory systems. At the end of the day, we cannot separate the body and the mind, and nowhere do we see this more clearly than during adolescent development. Biological changes put teens' emotions and attitudes in flux, which in turn affect their social behavior. Because these changes leave young people vulnerable to a path that ultimately leads to addiction, it is important to trace a teenager's or young adult's relationship to intoxication as it progresses from contemplation to experimentation to misuse to substance abuse and finally to addiction.

It Starts with Contemplation

In the contemplation stage, an adolescent both consciously and unconsciously prepares to use drugs, and during this time, adolescents watch their peers use alcohol or other drugs. Old friends might have begun using, and if they continue hanging out with the same people, they soon adapt to the new behavior. They may also learn that new friends are actively using drugs and they decide to continue the friendships, knowing that they are making their way into this new culture. They may wonder if it is safe, but they also see their peers share drugs with each other and listen to them talk about the high. From the position of those who are still on the outside, they observe other kids connect to each other in a different way, and in a way that non-users cannot share. In short, those in the contemplation stage are observing the "teen drug culture."

Teen drug culture is a brotherhood and sisterhood in which all people are equal—this is how it seems to the vulnerable adolescent observer. In this culture, teens can gain acceptance, fellowship, belonging and even a sense of family. In addition, they share the experience of the high they get from the drugs they use. It is an overall experience that connects them. For many teen and young adult drug users, it is this experience of connectedness that keeps them using drugs once they start. The drug culture forms part of the hook that catches teens in drug use and keeps them captive.

When adolescents witness social bonds being built and sustained through drug use, they are lured by the sense of belonging; early developmental wounds only amplify that drive to connect. As they continue to contemplate drug use, these vulnerable teens check out what it would be like to be a part of the group and use drugs. They may ask drug-using peers direct questions:

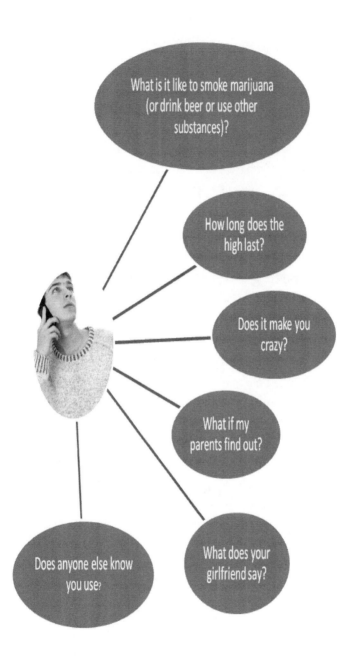

What is it like to smoke marijuana (or drink beer or use other substances)?

How long does the high last?

Does it make you crazy?

What if my parents find out?

What does your girlfriend say?

Does anyone else know you use?

90

As teens listen to the answers, they become more comfortable around their drug-using friends, and in turn, this information acts to ease their path toward use. At this stage, many begin to talk themselves into trying drugs. They are now closer to actual first use.

Moving closer to intoxication, they might start passing beers to other kids in the room, meanwhile abstaining from personal use, but smelling the beer when they pass it on. They do the same with marijuana, soon becoming accustomed to the smell of the burning marijuana joint or pipe as they pass it to a drug-using friend. More and more, they think about using drugs, and unless something breaks this early pattern, they eventually convince themselves that it is okay to try drugs.

For an older teen like Scott, who had always looked for a group to accept him, invite him to their gathering places, and introduce them to others, using drugs offered an alluring promise of a chance to belong. These offers of connectedness are especially effective when the only skill needed to enter and maintain standing in this group is to buy, use, and share drugs.

Remember, *during the contemplation stage a teen explores what it would be like to use drugs. However, in this stage no chemical use has yet occurred* (2).

When Contemplation Becomes Experimentation

Most people agree that adolescence is a time when young people search for their own identity through *experimenting* with new ideas, beliefs, values, and behaviors. Some adults will admit that adolescence was a painful time and they would just as soon forget their struggle with the extraordinary pressure from parents and peers. Drug use added another problem to an already difficult time.

In our offices, it is common for a parent to call and say, "I think my child is experimenting with drugs." When we ask how long the parent has suspected the child has been using drugs, the answer might indicate somewhere around one year. Unfortunately, this response reflects one of the myths perpetuated about adolescents: *adolescence is a time to experiment with drugs*. It is a widely held belief that a little experimentation is normal, which is the basis for the myth of "harmless use." This myth still prevails among today's parents, even in the face of the new research on the brain.

When parents talk about *one year* of drug use what they are describing is a situation that goes well beyond experimentation. The stage of adolescent drug use categorized as experimentation is not a stage at all. Strictly speaking, experimentation is recognized as a *one-time event*. Once the user has experienced intoxication, the experiment is over (3).

When adolescents decide to experiment (a one-time event) with drug use, they are getting high for the purpose of experiencing intoxication. As such, they ask, "Do I like the effects of this drug?" Again, once intoxication is attained, the experiment is over. This is when teens consider the results of this "research," and unconsciously or consciously conclude that they like it and want to do it again. Conversely, they might say, "I don't like this feeling," and that is the end of it. If they continue to use drugs beyond this single event they have progressed to the next stage of drug use: *misuse*.

The Journey from Experimenting to Misuse

When an adolescent has used drugs more than once, then they have progressed to the *misuse* stage. In this stage, their chemical use remains *infrequent*. They might use chemicals to mark occasions like New Year's Eve, graduation, Halloween, prom night, Homecoming, and so forth. They use the drug in order to get high—intoxicated—but they have not yet developed a trusting emotional relationship to intoxication (unlike what occurs during the *substance abuse* and *drug addiction* stages that follow and discussed below).

In the *misuse* stage, drug users might start to experience consequences of their chemical use, including teasing from friends, hangovers, minor injuries, and less open communication with parents and other family members. However, more severe consequences are also possible. It only takes one episode of intoxication to cause a car accident, or be sexually assaulted while intoxicated or passed out to commit violent acts or other crimes, or even to overdose.

Many young people with early developmental wounds or family histories of addiction can skip the *misuse* stage and move directly into substance abuse or drug addiction. In addition, frequency of use is only one factor to consider when evaluating the progression of chemical use. Another involves determining if the teenager has a relationship to intoxication. In the experimentation and misuse stages, a relationship to intoxication has not solidified. If, for example, young people suffer consequences from using drugs, they will quit using because they do not yet have a relationship to intoxication that is stronger than their desire to live according to their values. Family, friends, school, sports, work, and so forth represent more important elements in their lives that they do not want to put at risk.

When teens enter the stage of *substance abuse*, the users have developed an emotional relationship to intoxication (4). Whether or not these teenagers progress to substance abuse/addiction, *misuse* of chemicals is unhealthy and irresponsible behavior that puts adolescents at great risk. As stated earlier, even infrequent use of drugs or alcohol, regardless of the type of chemical, puts both teens and young adults at risk, even in the absence of a relationship to intoxication.

Substance Abuse

- According to DSM IV (5), the illness of substance abuse is defined as:
- ...a maladaptive pattern of substance use leading to clinically significant impairment or distress as manifested by one (or more) of the following, occurring within a 12-month period:

- 1. Recurrent substance use resulting in a failure to fulfill major role obligations at work, school, or home (such as repeated absences or poor work performance related to substance use; substance-related absences, suspensions, or expulsions from school; or neglect of children or household).
- 2. Recurrent substance use in situations in which it is physically hazardous (such as driving an automobile or operating a machine when impaired by substance use).
- 3. Recurrent substance-related legal problems (such as arrests for substance related disorderly conduct).
- 4. Continued substance use despite having persistent or recurrent social or interpersonal problems caused or exacerbated by the effects of the substance (for example, arguments with spouse about consequences of intoxication and physical fights).
- 5. Alternatively, the symptoms have never met the criteria for substance dependence for this class of substance.

- In the substance abuse stage, young people develop a regular schedule of using. For example, they might schedule time with their using friends on the weekends or on allowance day. The increasing use and scheduling occur because they have established an ongoing relationship to intoxication. This means they have begun to trust chemicals, based on their experience with them.

Experimentation and misuse has reinforced the idea that drugs relieve stress, anxiety, depression, anger, loneliness, and the feeling adolescents mention most, boredom. To these young people, chemicals are loyal and always there for them, although they do not recognize their drug use as being related to their feelings. In fact, in the early phase of treatment for substance abuse and addiction, most adolescents deny that their drug use is related to their emotional states, despite the fact that drugs have reliably changed and soothed their unpleasant affective states.

Because personal identity is now being reorganized within the context of peer relationships, along with early developmental wounds, adolescents often work through the following questions:

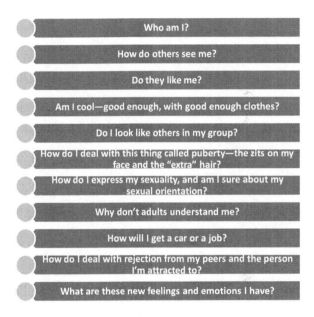

- Who am I?
- How do others see me?
- Do they like me?
- Am I cool—good enough, with good enough clothes?
- Do I look like others in my group?
- How do I deal with this thing called puberty—the zits on my face and the "extra" hair?
- How do I express my sexuality, and am I sure about my sexual orientation?
- Why don't adults understand me?
- How will I get a car or a job?
- How do I deal with rejection from my peers and the person I'm attracted to?
- What are these new feelings and emotions I have?

From ancient sages to modern psychologists, virtually everyone has written about adolescent anxiety. We all remember it. Drug-using teens have learned that intoxication takes the edge off their emotions during this taxing time of life.

Paradoxically, drugs, drug dealers, and the drug culture have reliably responded to teens' unpleasant affective states. The power of intoxication itself teaches drug users that they can fully trust the drugs as reliable, predictable, and soothing. This is the source of the pathological relationship drug users develop with intoxication. Once it is established, it is far more important than any other relationships, including those with parents, siblings, friends, teachers, coaches, youth workers, and ministers/rabbis.

It is also the fun, associated "good times," and the temporary euphoria that motivate teen and young adult users to continue their trusting relationship with drugs. The pleasure, fun, and excitement derived from drug use far exceed what riding their bikes and playing video games can provide. Moreover, young people experience their deregulated affective states being soothed through the drug, and since they have not experienced the normal emotional regulation in healthy relationships, the drug is linked with feeling better—at least for a little while. Finally, drugs offer them what they have lacked, specifically, a culture of acceptance and belonging.

In the substance abuse stage, users begin losing the connection between chemical use and undesirable consequences. By this time, they might find themselves in trouble at home or with the law. Almost inevitably, teens find themselves at odds with friends, teachers, the school system, or their bosses on their jobs. Despite these negative consequences of drug use, they continue to use because they now have a pathological relationship to intoxication. While the connection between drug use and consequences becomes increasingly unclear for users, other people see the changes in this person more clearly.

Diagnostically, substance abuse is simply defined as using chemicals despite the fact that drugs create ongoing negative consequences. But on a deeper level, we recognize that substance abuse can simultaneously result from and be the etiology of an emotional illness. Consider the following three variables:

1. *The drug use circumvents the user from developing their own internal skills to identify, experience, express, and cope with emotions.*

During adolescence, teens experience a broader range of emotions and a greater depth of emotions—as compared to the preteen years. As an important developmental task, teens must learn how to *identify* what they are feeling, allow themselves to *experience* the feeling, *express* the feeling in interpersonal relationships, and generally *cope* with it. Typically, young people feel romantic attraction, fear of romantic rejection, anxiety about getting a job, anxiety about school and social pressures, or even boredom, but most learn to work through it. They talk with their friends about what is going on, and through these peer relationships, emotions become normalized. Kids engage in brainstorming as they try to work together to find alternatives to boredom, and they share new skills to ameliorate anxieties around employment, relationships, and so on.

In that process, teens work through this developmental task, but juvenile-onset-substance-use circumvents the course of maturation and contributes to the arrested emotional development we see in addicts as they leave their teen years and enter young adulthood, and continues in addicts of all ages. When teens start to use drugs to disconnect from what they feel or change the way they feel, they eventually overly rely on substances to cope. Adolescents and the adults around them often miss this misplaced coping mechanism, and the teens themselves certainly are unaware that drug use is interrupting their normal maturation process.

When young people are anxious or bored, these feeling states go away when they become intoxicated; this robs them of intrinsic motivation to work through the this stage of development. In other words, when adolescents are high, they are satisfied—no more uncomfortable emotional state exists. The drug has made it go away.

Unfortunately, over time and with each use, teens reinforce the idea that drugs will change the way they feel; they soon learn to over rely on the drug to cope and self-medicate. With each use, they undermine the natural development of coping skills that are supposed to occur at this time in their life.

For some adolescents, a preexisting setup magnifies this problem and fuels the drive to use drugs. These are the teens we see who have grown up with an inability to express emotions in words (alexithymia) because of dismissive-avoidant early childhood relationships. When parents are indifferent, non-empathic, and split off from emotion, their children do not have the language with which to talk about emotion.

A major treatment component during early sobriety involves unlocking the emotional arrest through teaching those in recovery the skills needed to identify, experience, express, and cope with emotions. One of the most common clichés—or truisms—in the 12-step communities of AA and NA is: *When you quit using drugs, you are emotionally the age you were when you started using.* Both those with long-term recovery and addiction counselors recognize that emotional growth stops when drug use starts. My experience in clinical practice confirms that this emotional arrest is more profound with juvenile onset vs. adult onset of use.

2. *Drug use distorts the user's emotions.*

Pain is a built-in biological safeguard for physical survival, which is why we feel pain and recoil when we touch a hot stove. We also have safeguards for our emotional, psychological, and spiritual survival. If we devise and execute a plan to steal from someone, we feel anxiety, guilt, and shame. Those feelings are barometers that let us know that what we are about to do, or are in the process of doing, is neither healthy nor consistent with our values. However, in the stage of substance abuse and addiction, the user loses that barometer and disconnects from unpleasant emotions. It becomes easy, then, to engage in lying, conning, manipulating, and even stealing—and with an increasingly carefree attitude. With unpleasant emotions gone, the users are in denial, that is, they are misinformed about the choices they make and do not recognize a need for change.

3. *Values change.*

Drug abuse and addiction hijack a young person's values. As the relationship to intoxication increases, it becomes more important than work, family, school, non-using friends, sports, or other activities. During this process, the user sees the change, not because of the drug use, but because of everyone else: "My teacher is picking on me…" or "my parents are tripping…"

It is fascinating to watch how intensely young drug abusers and addicts hate their parents for putting them in treatment. The parents feel beaten up and wounded as the young people fight to protect their relationship to intoxication. They push away parents and anyone who stands in the way of the relationship. At the start of treatment many of these individuals claim they do not care about their parents. However, six months of sobriety later, their values have changed. They often move from hating their parents to admitting that one of their biggest regrets is what their drug use put their parents through. Moreover, earning back parental trust is one of the biggest rewards of sobriety.

Looking at the three items listed above, we can see that young users develop a trusting relationship to intoxication, stunt their emotional growth, and disconnect from some of their emotions. Putting all this together, it is easy to see that using drugs has emotionally high-jacked the teen, thus amplifying an "I don't care" attitude. To undo the damage, young people need to be sober, which means their relationship to intoxication must be broken. Once this occurs, develop can continue.

Remember: *substance abuse* means using chemicals despite having experienced negative consequences: being grounded at home, suspended from school, engaged in criminal behavior, or injured in an accident or violent act, using more and more often, and having an emotional relationship to intoxication.

Drug Addiction

- According to DSM IV (6), Addiction (termed *substance dependence* by the American Psychiatric Association) is defined as:
- *A maladaptive pattern of substance use leading to clinically significant impairment or distress, as manifested by three (or more) of the following, occurring any time in the same 12-month period:*
- *1.   Tolerance, as defined by either of the following:*
- *(a) A need for markedly increased amounts of the substance to achieve intoxication or the desired effect or (b) Markedly diminished effect with continued use of the same amount of the substance.*
- *2.   Withdrawal, as manifested by either of the following:*
- *(a) The characteristic withdrawal syndrome for the substance or (b) The same (or closely related) substance is taken to relieve or avoid withdrawal symptoms.*
- *3.   The substance is often taken in larger amounts or over a longer period than intended.*
- *4.   There is a persistent desire or unsuccessful efforts to cut down or control substance use.*
- *5.   A great deal of time is spent in activities necessary to obtain the substance, use the substance, or recover from its effects.*
- *6.   Important social, occupational, or recreational activities are given up or reduced because of substance use.*
- *7.   The substance use is continued despite knowledge of having a persistent physical or psychological problem that is likely to have been caused or exacerbated by the substance (for example, current cocaine use despite recognition of cocaine-induced depression or continued drinking despite recognition that an ulcer was made worse by alcohol consumption).*

DSM IV criteria for substance dependence also include several specifiers, one of which outlines whether substance dependence occurs with physiologic dependence (evidence of tolerance or withdrawal) or without physiologic dependence (no evidence of tolerance or withdrawal). In addition, remission categories are classified into four subtypes: 1, full, 2, early partial, 3, sustained, and 4, sustained partial.

The categories are based on whether the criteria for abuse or dependence have been met and over what timeframe. The remission category can also be applied to patients receiving agonist therapy (such as methadone maintenance) or for those living in a controlled, drug-free environment.

Of course, we need to know more about adolescent addiction than what the DSM IV offers. For example, adolescents are not addicted to marijuana, alcohol, ecstasy, or cocaine. The name of the drug is an illusion, because young people are *addicted to intoxication.* We have put too much focus on the specific drugs used, as if names are important. To amplify, if a teen is addicted to marijuana or heroin, he or she is addicted. Both drugs are harmful, although one may sound scarier than the other. Based on my observation, 95% of the effects of the drugs are the same, but many focus far too much focus on the 5% difference. The symptoms of dependence are essentially the same regardless of the substance, and when we watch how they play out we see that once addicted, the patterns of behavior are all the same. Ultimately, emphasizing the difference leads to minimizing drugs like marijuana and alcohol and labeling their use "normal experimentation."

To make the point that the name of the drug is an illusion, I ask you to tell me which drug my client is using based on experiences and effects on his life?

- He is now obsessed with using.
- He has started to use more of it over time to get the desired effect.
- He has pulled away from his family more and more, and no longer plays a once favorite sport.
- His grades have plummeted, and now he skips school.
- He pulled away from former friends and now counts on his drug-using buddies.
- His money is going to drugs—and he lies, cheats, and manipulates his parents to get more money for more drugs.

So, which drug is my client using? *Any* drug.

Biological properties differ from drug to drug, but in the hands of a substance abuser or addict, the symptoms are primarily all the same. If you were to ask my client if he would stop using if his drug of choice disappeared from the face of the earth, the answer is no. He was never hooked on "his" drug; he was hooked on intoxication.

This issue is critical because marijuana and alcohol are the most minimized drugs that young people typically abuse. The majority of kids I have referred to inpatient treatment used marijuana. I did not refer these individuals because of legal or moral issues involved in drug use. They entered inpatient treatment because their relationship to intoxication had a significant negative impact on school, family, money, sports, and so forth. Furthermore, of the 20 teenage clients who have died, 18 deaths were related to alcohol. However, many within the professional community, such as therapists, school counselors, coaches, medical doctors, and others, continue minimizing marijuana and alcohol. This is true on college campuses, where in 2009, 1,825 deaths were caused by alcohol poisoning and accidents related to intoxication.

The Common Denominator

Dishonesty is the currency of adolescent drug use. Drug addicted teens and even young adults generally lack marketable skills to earn their own money to pay for drugs. They cannot openly tell their parents and other adults that they like to wake up in the morning and smoke marijuana—known as "wake n bake." Obviously, they cannot tell teachers they get high before class because it is so much fun. Teens are well aware that adults disapprove of drug use, so being honest about it means the beginning of the end of drug use. Therefore, adolescent drug users who want to continue getting high have no alternative to dishonesty.

Juvenile Onset Substance Use Contributes to a Rapid Progression from Experimentation to Drug Addiction: Contrasts between Adults and Adolescents in the Progression of Addiction & Denial

Adolescent	**Adult**
Rapid Progression	Slower Progression
Glorification of Use	Minimization of Use
Multiple Drugs Used	Single Drug Used
Social Activities *are* Chemical Use	Social Activities Include Use
Developmental Issues Cloud Insight	Professional/Social Standing Cloud Insight
Early Arrest of Emotional Development	Minimal Arrest of Emotional Development

Gust, Smith (2008) Effective Outpatient Treatment for Adolescents (7)

Based on current research, it appears that juvenile-onset-users progress more rapidly to addiction than adult-onset-users. We can attribute this difference to developmental issues in adolescent biology and psychology, plus environmental factors. Here's a closer look:

- **For adolescent users, drug use alone is a social event**

  Adults might use, misuse, or abuse chemicals at social occasions such as weddings, New Year's Eve parties, or on Super Bowl Sunday, and using the chemical represents only a part of the social event. By contrast, for drug-using adolescents, intoxication itself *is* the social event. An adult will invite a friend over to watch the big game, but a teen calls another teen and says, "Hey Joe, come on over and let's get high." Then they might add another person. "And why you don't call Tom and we'll get stoned with him, too."

  As young people have more and more of these "social events," they use with increasing frequency, and their social group supports their denial. This is also why they end up moving away from their non-user friends and other activities. As explained earlier, insecurely attached teens who struggle with developing peer relationship find acceptance within the drug culture.

- **Adolescents use a combination of drugs**

  For the most part, adults use one drug, such as alcohol, but young drug users most likely use a combination of drugs, known as *poly-drug use*, *garbage can syndrome*, or *garbage can junkie*. Because several different neurotransmitters in the brain are damaged by different drugs, intoxication resulting from different drugs increases tolerance and the need for more and more drugs to get the desired effect. This is why poly-drug use fuels the rapid progression.

- **The adolescent's environment can promote drug use rather than inhibit it**

  Adults have to wake up, feed their kids, go to work, pay bills, make dinner, and are responsible for the family. This structure tends to make frequent drug use difficult. However, the primary structure for teens is school, which is also the place to buy and sell drugs, talk about the fun times of being high on drugs, and plan new times to get high. Therefore, an adolescent's school structure, which we might erroneously assume inhibits drug use, actually is a part of the problem. Easy availability of drugs significantly contributes to the progression of drug use.

- **Genetics and family history**

  Today we know drug addiction can be traced through family histories. This may be in the form of a specific set of genes or imbalance in brain chemistry inherited generationally, or it may come from growing up in an environment in which dysfunction from substance abuse has generationally shaped the psychological structure, affect regulation, and interpersonal style of the family. In all these cases, we can count family history as a significant risk factor.

Adolescent Denial

The defense mechanism of denial protects users from seeing the consequences of their use, as well preventing them from experiencing varying degrees of guilt and anxiety surrounding their drug use. If they accurately perceived the effects of their drug use, they would have to quit. Therefore, denial obscures insight and protects use.

We differentiate denial from dishonesty. Denial is an unconscious defense mechanism that is honest self-deception.

105

Users believe their words when they claim that using drugs is not a problem, which is classic denial.

On the other hand, a young user might arrive late to a session, staggering in smelling like alcohol and slurring her speech. But when asked if she has been drinking, she says no. That is not denial, it is dishonesty—lying. And young people know they are lying. It is important not to confuse dishonesty and denial.

Variables Contributing to Denial

Drug use prevents users from experiencing the consequences of the use. Young people with a substance use disorder might become disconnected from their emotions, so they do not fully experience of the range and depth of their negative emotions while they use. This means they are disconnected from the consequences of drug use as seen in school, sports, family relationships, their finances, the legal system, and so forth. When drug-abusing teens and young adults are disconnected from guilt, anxiety, shame, embarrassment, and so forth, then they do not receive valuable information (feedback) about their judgment, choices, and behavior. They do not learn from their bad choices, either.

When normal drug-free kids use poor judgment and make bad choices, they experience anxiety, guilt, anxiety, shame, embarrassment, and so forth. Those unpleasant feelings tell them not to repeat the same choice. The substance abuser or addict is disconnected from that experience.

Alexithymia

Children have a vast capacity for development. Three billion neurons fire in the first year of life and half of them die off by the end of that first year. Early neuro-development, a time in which neurons are blooming and pruning, is *experience dependent*, meaning that neurons bloom when supported by the caregiver and the environment, but they prune in the absence of support. Ideally, children express their emotional selves to their caregivers, who mirror back their expressions. This means that they attune to the child's experience. This is done by mirroring and tuning into their children's vocal cues, motor cues, pace of vocalization, expressions, tone of vocal expression, and affective state, along with soothing through warmth and consistent comforting responses. This attunement allows children's emotional development to bloom.

In this ideal situation, children's relationship to their internal emotional states allows the freedom to build the parent-child relationship. When the caregiver provides this supportive process, the *insula* develops and builds the neural networks in the right hemisphere of the brain, the seat of implicit memory. An unconscious memory forms that it is safe to connect to emotions, experience them, express them, and turn to others for emotional regulation.

In the absence of this attunement experience, these regulatory processes are stunted, which means that children's attachment organization can become disconnected to their internal experiences. They learn that expressing feelings is not okay. In fact, in early childhood, expressing emotions without attunement can lead to shame in the child. If the attachment relationship does not allow children to express their feelings, then the children still do whatever it takes to preserve the attachment. In this situation, they learn to stuff, ignore, split off from and avoid verbal expression of their emotions (8), which ultimately results in alexithymia (9) (10). This concept is critical, because being disconnected from emotions fuels denial.

The Adolescent Frame of Reference

Young people who long to feel a connection to others are at great risk of falling into the comforting, nonjudgmental, welcoming drug culture. Once a relationship to intoxication and the drug culture have developed, users skillfully, yet unconsciously, create a world in which they are surrounded by increasing numbers of people who act as they do, that is, use drugs. That is why over time, users begin to believe their own claim that "everyone I know uses drugs." It has become the truth for drug-users who fail to see the cause and effect relationship. Of course, everyone they know uses drugs. They have created that very world to make it so.

Young People do not Want to Give Up the Rewards

Being high feels good, and brings bio-psycho-social pleasures for the adolescent and young adult drug user:

- Biologically, drugs manipulate soothing neurotransmitters, dopamine, norepinephrine, GABA, serotonin, or endorphins in a way that creates intoxicating euphoria.
- Psychologically, this experience medicates, regulates, and soothes unpleasant emotional states for teens.
- Socially, drug culture is nonjudgmental, accepting, and offers instant brother/sisterhood and even family, thus satisfying the need to belong.

When Young People do not Experience Consequences

Unfortunately, in order to recognize a problem and reach out for help, some drug users need to experience painful consequences on many levels: biological, social, emotional, relational, financial and/or legal. Those in the recovery community often say that an addict has to hit bottom before they can accept help. However, those of us who work with adolescent users believe it is our job to work with them and their families to help lift the bottom.

Teens and young adults with drug problems are not supposed to want to quit, so for many, the impetus for help comes only when one of the systems they deal with holds them accountable. These systems include family, friends, school, the legal system, coaches, employers, and so forth. Unfortunately, many within these systems subscribe to the notion that drug use is a normal part of the teenage and young adult years, thereby making it possible for some to avoid the natural consequences of their use. For example, parents might make excuses to the school, and therapists might make excuses to the probation officers, who in turn make excuses to the judge.

To be sure, these actions are done with good intentions. A teacher or judge might say: "I don't want this young man to endure the hardship of being kicked out of school or going to juvenile hall." But in fact, those natural consequences could offer the addict a jolt into awareness of the need for change.

Chapter 4: Notes

1. American Psychiatric Association: *Diagnostic and Statistical Manual of Mental Disorders*, Fourth Edition, Text Revision. Washington, DC, American Psychiatric Association. (2000).

2. Gust, Walker, Daily, *How to Help Your Child Become Drug Free: A Guide for Parents of Adolescents & Young Adults with Substance Abuse or Addiction.* (2006).

3. Gust, Walker, Daily (2006).

4. Gust, Walker, Daily (2006).

5. American Psychiatric Association: *Diagnostic and Statistical Manual of Mental Disorders*, Fourth Edition. (2000).

6. American Psychiatric Association: *Diagnostic and Statistical Manual of Mental Disorders*, Fourth Edition (2000).

7. Gust, Smith, *Effective Outpatient Treatment for Adolescents* (2008).

8. Siegel, D. J. *The Developing Mind* (The Guilford Press, 1999).

9. Cozolino, *The Neuroscience of Human Relationships: Attachment and the Developing Social Brain.* (W.W. Norton & Company, 2006.

10. Bowlby, J. Maternal care and mental health. *World Health Organization Monograph* (Serial No. 2, 1951).

Chapter 5
Attachment Classifications & Internal Working Model

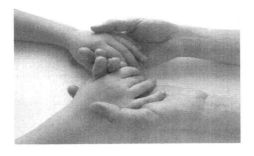

Many of the most intense emotions arise during the formation, the maintenance, the disruption, and the renewal of attachment relationships. The formation of a bond is described as falling in love, maintaining a bond as loving someone, and losing a partner as grieving over someone. Similarly, threat of loss arouses anxiety and actual loss gives rise to sorrow; whilst each of these situations is likely to arouse anger. The unchallenged maintenance of a bond is experienced as a source of joy (1).

When dealing with adolescent and young adult substance abusers and addicts, it is important to keep in mind their *pathological relationship to intoxication*. As previously explained, the names of the drugs they use are irrelevant. Concern with particular drugs is nothing more than an illusion that allows parents and therapists, along with the general public, to judge one drug as either less harmful or worse than another. This attitude builds mythologies around certain drugs based on false ideas. However, young people do not become hooked on marijuana, alcohol, Ecstasy, pain killers, or inhalants. In fact, when adolescents anticipate drug-testing, they often switch from one drug to another to avoid detection, thus holding on to and protecting their *relationship to intoxication*.

Adolescents and young adults are attached to intoxication, regardless of the drug, for soothing, to the point of choosing their relationship to intoxication over their relationship to school, family, friends, sports, money, and even freedom. Intoxication wins, even when drug use creates negative consequences, including after users have experienced brushes with the law. The question is why adolescents continue to carefully guard this relationship to intoxication. What purpose does it serve? What does it really offer them, especially in light of a host of negative consequences?

Intoxication offers substance abusers soothing in the form of affect regulation, new social relationships within the drug culture, and for many, an identity. In other words, their experience with drugs offers emotional comfort, allows them to connect to people who "get" them, and through this, they have a way to define themselves. This is all one big hook that replaces failed attachments, and this relationship with the perceived "rewards" of intoxication ultimately arrests development.

When Attachment Goes Awry

Whether they are conscious of it or not, adults have a general idea of attachment theory and its application to the "self." For example, when we say, "Oh, I know Joe—he's really insecure," we're expressing an element of attachment theory. Over fifty years ago, John Bowlby, a British child psychiatrist began writing about his theories of attachment, and in the 1960s, Mary Ainsworth advanced the work by applying the theories to empirical research. Ainsworth's work linked naturalistic observation techniques to the study of the relationship between mothers and their children when together, separated, and during reunion. Named the "Strange Situation" study, it began in Uganda and continued in Baltimore, and became one of the most

112

widely reviewed and replicated studies in developmental psychology (2).

Designed to understand children's attachment and exploratory behavior during different stressful scenarios, Ainsworth introduced a toddler (12 – 20 months of age) to the so-called strange situation, which occurred in stages:

- A toddler and mother entered a room, and then the child's degree of exploration was observed.
- Next, a stranger entered the room and began playing with the child, followed by the child's mother quietly leaving the room (separation).
- After a couple minutes, the mother returned (reunion) and the stranger left.
- Then the parent left the toddler alone (second separation) and the stranger reentered the room.
- Finally, the parent returned and the stranger left (second reunion).

From observing the children, Ainsworth noted that children responded in different ways when the mother returned; these observations led to different classification groups of attachment outlined in the chart below.

Strange Situation Classification Groups (3)

Group	Brief description
Secure (B) (4)	Uses mother as secure base for exploration. Separation: Signs of missing parent, especially during the second separation. Reunion: Actively greets parent with smile, vocalization, or gesture. If upset, signals or seeks contact with parent.

	Once comforted, returns to exploration.
Avoidant (A) (5)	Explores readily, little display of affect or secure-base behavior. Separation: Responds minimally, little visible distress when left alone. Reunion: Looks away from, actively avoids parent; often focuses on toys. If picked up, may stiffen, lean away. Seeks distance from parent, often interested instead in toys.
Ambivalent or resistant (C) (6)	Visibly distressed upon entering room, often fretful or passive; fails to engage in exploration. Separation: Unsettled, distressed. Reunion: May alternate bids for contact with signs of angry rejection, tantrums; or may appear passive or too upset to signal, make contact. Fails to find comfort in parent.
Disorganized/disoriented (D) (7)	Behavior appears to lack observational goal, intention, or explanation—for example, contradictory sequences or simultaneous behavioral displays; incomplete, interrupted movement; streotypies [repetitive or ritualistic behavior]; freezing/stilling; direct indications of fear/apprehension of parent; confusion, disorientation. Most characteristic is lack of a coherent attachment strategy, despite the fact that the baby may reveal the underlying patterns of organized attachment (A, B, C).

Adolescents and the "Strange Situation"

The adolescent years may well be a naturally occurring *strange situation*. During the elementary school experience, most kids are with the same students and teacher each day. At this age, most children have not formed romantic attachments, and the social skills necessary to connect with their peers are fairly simple. However, by the time they arrive in high school and have entered the adolescent developmental stage, they may have less stability in their day. For example, they may be with different sets of kids in each class and may change classrooms, teachers, and subjects four to six times a day. While social cliques form at fairly young ages, at least for girls, these relationships intensify during high school, along with romantic feelings and dating. Teens, and young adults, too, need more sophisticated social skills to form and maintain relationships. This is a difficult time even for secure teenagers, but for insecurely attached young people, this time can bring about a heightened state of anxiety, and taxes what resources they have to adapt to these new situations.

Attachment is related to the quality of peer relationships and peer competence across developmental periods (8); specifically, peer relationships influence popularity (9); aggression (10) (11); self-esteem (12), and the emergence of mental health issues such as depression during adolescence (13).

The parent-child relationship is also correlated with peer social skills in preschoolers (14). Researchers have found that children securely attached to their mothers more often believe that their peers have positive intent in ambiguous situations (15). This research supports the idea that early child-caregiver attachment experiences have far reaching implications for future peer interactions. Secure attachments appear to foster social competence during middle childhood, and likely having an impact on the quality of children's friendships (16).

A self-report study of fifth graders showed that security with one's mother relates to fifth graders' acceptance by their peers and their behavior with friends (17), and secure adolescents (18) are also associated with peer competence.

Clinicians can glean a great deal from early childhood attachment classifications; however, within the classification, each individual has a unique subjective Internal Working Model (IWM). The IWM becomes the filter through which the children see themselves and others in their surroundings.

The Internal Working Model (IWM)

Attachment theory (19) (20) (21) (22) has profoundly influenced research and theories about the nature of human relationships throughout life. The primary assumption of attachment theory is that humans form close emotional bonds in the interest of survival. In other words, human cultures need bonds to survive collectively and as individuals. These bonds also allow us to develop and maintain mental representations of the self and of others, or *internal working models* (IWM) (23).

The IWM concept forms the foundation for understanding how attachment processes operate in adult relationships. The IWM reflects what we believe about ourselves, others, and the world and influences what we expect of ourselves, others, and the world in general, and then directs our responses. It is generally thought that IWMs include specific *content* about attachment figures and the self, stored within a well organized representational *structure* (24) (25) (26) (27).

The IWM begins to form immediately after birth and is based on experiences with others and the outcomes we try to elicit. In the working model of the self, a key feature is the notion of how acceptable or unacceptable he himself is in the eyes of his attachment figures (28). The IWM is hypothesized to operate primarily outside of conscious awareness (29) (30) (31) (32).

116

This hypothesis is supported by neuroscience showing that the brain is right-hemisphere dominant in neural network development during a child's first 18 months. The child's environment directs the blooming or pruning of neurons and neural networks during this phase of development, and this later plays out as our unconscious IWM (33) (34).

"Am I the gleam in my care-givers' eyes or their source of frustration?" An infant that experiences frequent abuse or neglect can develop a negative internal working model that says: *"No one cares about me, I am unlovable, and people who are supposed to love me only hurt or reject me. It doesn't matter what I do or say, it is ineffective or not good enough. I can't trust people."*

If this model of self, others, and the world, which forms the beliefs about how things work in the child's world, goes uncorrected, the result may be a child growing to adulthood with low self-esteem. The child may become either overly dependent or independent; overreacts to situations; sabotages relationships, jobs, and successes; gives up easily; abuses drugs, and so forth. Conversely infants who receive consistent, responsive, attuned nurturing from their caregivers are most likely to develop a positive IWM. Other research (35) illuminates the parallels between the child-caregiver relationship and the relationship between romantic attachments.

Preteens may or may not have a positive IWM as they cross the bridge into adolescence; even with a positive IWM, most find these years challenging. With a negative IWM, it is even more challenging for a teen to navigate the turbulent waters of adolescence. The role of clinicians working with young people, a role Bowbly described as being analogous to the parent, involves offering an experience through the client-therapist relationship that reorganizes the IWM and moves the client to a place of *earned secure attachment.*

Earned Secure Attachment

I had a weak father, sadistic sergeants,
destructive male friendships, emasculating
girlfriends, a wonderful wife, and three
terrific children. Where did I go right?
Jules Feiffer, Satirist and Illustrator

Internal working models (IWM) have been shown to be fairly stable throughout the life span. However, research has shown that it can change from insecure to secure (36) (37), the "earned" element in "earned secure attachment." This was illustrated by Mary Main and her colleagues in her study of parents and their six-year-old children. Through administrating the Adult Attachment Interview (AAI) these researchers found that many parents had themselves experienced inconsistent or non-attuned parenting. However, despite their challenging early attachment experiences with their caregivers, through the process of integrating the experiences they emerged as securely attached adults. Main found that these parents provided a relational experience to their offspring that resulted in their children becoming securely attached.

According to Main, the primary characteristics of earned secure attachment in the AAI are meta-cognitive and integrative thinking, and both cognitive capacities are built upon multiple skills. Such skills include the capacity to observe one's own mental states, an ability to articulate a theory of another person's mind, a sense of mastery, and personal efficacy. These abilities are the underpinnings of psychotherapy. Since many addicted young people are split off from their internal processes and needs, therapists must help build their clients' reflective capacity, which is then put into practice during therapy.

Secure attachment then allows the individual to feel safe enough to explore, examine and deconstruct early childhood issues, relationships, and affective responses. The AAI is based on Main's insight that it is not only the content of what is said, but how it is said, that provide data for determining attachments. In other words, therapists can assess reflective capacity and self-understanding by observing the way a question is answered.

When working with insecurely attached young people with substance abuse disorders, therapists can intervene by focusing on helping them become "earned secure." Bowlby saw working models as largely stable because they are laid down early in life and are largely unconscious, but he did not see them as unchangeable (38) (39). The term "earned secure" thus describes individuals whose childhood insecure attachment working models have become secure, usually as a result of experience in supportive relationships and/or therapy (40).

Teens and young adults often show up for alcohol and drug abuse counseling with a cautious attitude. Then, through the therapeutic experience, these young people learn they can trust the therapist, who is helping to build a secure base in clients' IWM. This altered IWM becomes the foundation for teenagers' ability to take a risk to explore their issues and become more open to letting go of their relationship to intoxication. In terms of soothing, they also learn to turn to the therapist and possibly other supportive resources, such as youth groups, 12-step meetings, and so forth, rather than turning to drugs, dealers, and drug culture.

Chapter 5: Notes

1. Bowlby, J. *The Making and Breaking of Affectional Bonds*, p. 130 (London: Tavistock, 1979).

2. Ainsworth, M.D.S., Blehar, M.C., Waters, E., & Wall, S. Patterns of Attachment: A Psychological Study of the Strange Situation. (Hillsdale, NJ: Erlbaum, 1978).

3. Cassidy J., Shaver P. R., *Handbook of attachment,* p. 291 (Guilford Press, New York, 1999).

4. Ainsworth, M.D.S., Blehar, M.C., Waters, E., & Wall, S., 1978.

5. Ainsworth, M.D.S., Blehar, M.C., Waters, E., & Wall, S., 1978.
6. Ainsworth, M.D.S., Blehar, M.C., Waters, E., & Wall, S., 1978.
7. Main, M., Solomon, J., Procedures for identifying infants as disorganized/disoriented during the Ainsworth strange situation. In M. T. Greenberg, D. Cicchetti, & E. M. Cummings (Eds.), *Attachment in the preschool years* (pp. 121-160). (Chicago: University of Chicago Press, 1990).

8. Elicker, J., Englund, M., & Sroufe, L. A. Predicting peer competence and peer relationships in childhood from early parent-child relationships. In R. Parke & G. Ladd (Eds.), *Family-peer relationships: Modes of linkage* (pp. 77-106). Hillsdale, NJ: Erlbaum, (1992).

9. DeMulder, E. K., Denham, S., Schmidt, M., & Mitchell, J. (2000) Q-sort assessment of attachment security during the preschool years: Links from home to school. *Developmental Psychology*, 36(2), 274-282.

10. Cohn, D. A., (1990) Child-mother attachment of six-year-olds and social competence at school. *Child Development*, 61, 152-162.

11. DeMulder, E. K., Denham, S., Schmidt, M., & Mitchell, J. (2000). Q-sort assessment of attachment security during the

preschool years: Links from home to school. *Developmental Psychology,* 36(2), 274-282.

12. Armsden, G. C., & Greenberg, M. T. (1987). The inventory of parent and peer attachment: Individual differences and their relationship to psychological well-being in adolescence. *Journal of Youth and Adolescence*, 16(5), 427-454.

13. Nada Raja, S., McGee, R., & Stanton, W. R. (1992). Perceived attachments to parents and peers and psychological well-being in adolescence. *Journal of Youth and Adolescence*, 21(4), 471-485.

14. Pianta, R. C., Nimetz, S. L., & Bennett, E. (1997). Mother-child relationships, teacher-child relationships, and school outcomes in preschool and kindergarten. *Early Childhood Research Quarterly*, 12, 263-280.

15. Cassidy, J., Kirsh, S. J., Scolton, K. L., & Parke, R. D. (1996). Attachment representations of peer relationships. *Developmental Psychology*, 32(5), 892-904.

16. Freitag, M. K., Belsky, J., Grossmann, K., Grossmann, K. E., & Scheuerer-Englisch, H. (1996). Continuity in parent-child relationships from infancy to middle childhood and relations with friendship competence. *Child Development*, 67(4), 1437-1454.

17. Kerns, K. A., Cole, A., & Klepac, L. (1996). Peer relationships and preadolescents' perceptions of security in the child-mother relationship. *Developmental Psychology*, 32(3), 457-466.

18. Allen, J. P., Moore, C., Kuperminc, G., & Bell, K. (1998). Attachment and adolescent psychosocial functioning. *Child Development, 69(5),* 1406-1419.

19. Bowlby, J. *Attachment and loss: Vol 1. Attachment.* (New York: Basic Books, 1969).

20. Bowlby, J. *Attachment and loss: Vol. 2. Separation: Anxiety and anger.* (New York: Basic Books, 1973).

21. Bowlby, J. *The Making and Breaking of Affectional Bonds.* (London: Tavistock, 1979).

22. Bowlby, J. *Attachment and loss: Vol. 3. Loss: Sadness and depression.* (New York: Basic Books, 1980).

23. Review: *General Psychology* (Educational Publishing Foundation, 2000) Vol. 4, No. 2, 155-175, The Internal Working Models Concept: What Do We Really Know About the Self in Relation to Others? Authors: Paula R, Pietromonaco & Lisa Feldman Barrett.

24. Bowlby, J. *A Secure Base.* (New York: Basic Books, 1988).

25. Bretherton, I. Attachment theory: Retrospect and prospect. *Monographs of the Society for Research in Child Development*, 50(1-2, Serial No. 209) 1985.

26. Bretherton, I. Open communication and internal working models: Their role in the development of attachment relationships. In R. A. Thompson (Ed.), *Nebraska Symposium on Motivation* (Vol. 36, pp. 57-113). (Lincoln Nebraska: University of Nebraska Press, 1990).

27. Collins, N., & Read, S. J. Cognitive representations of attachment: The structure and function of working models. In D. Perlman & K. Bartholomew (Eds.), *Advances in personal relationships* (Vol. 5, pp. 53-90). (London: Jessica Kingsley, 1994).

28. Bowlby, 1973, p. 204.

29. Bowlby, 1980.

30. Bretherton, I. 1985.

31. Bretherton, I. 1990.

32. Main, M., Kaplan, K., & Cassidy, J. Security in infancy, childhood, and adulthood: A move to the level of representation. *Monographs of the Society for Research in Child Development,* 50(1-2, Serial No. 209) 1985.

33. Cozolino, *The Neuroscience of Human Relationships: Attachment and the Developing Social Brain.* (New York: W.W. Norton, 2006).

34. Schore, A.N. *Affect Dysregulation and Disorders of the Self.* (New York: W.W. Norton, 2003).

35. Hazan, C., & Shaver, P. R. Romantic love conceptualized as an attachment process. *Journal of Personality and Social Psychology,* 52, 511- 524 (1987).

36. Main, M., Kaplan, N., Cassidy, J., Security in infancy, childhood, and adulthood: a move to the level of representation. In Bretherton, I., & Waters, E., (Eds.) Growing points of attachment theory and research: *Monographs of the Society for Research in Child Development,* 50, 66-104 (1985).

37. Hesse, E., The adult attachment interview: Historical and current perspectives. In J. Cassidy & P. Shaver (Eds.) *Handbook of Attachment: theory, research and clinical implications,* pp. 395-414 (New York: Guilford, 1999).

38. Bowlby, J. "The Role of Attachment in Personality Development" (from *A Secure Base: Parent-Child*

Attachment and Healthy Human Development, Lecture 7, pp. 119-136) (New York: Basic Books 1988).

39. Bowlby, J. 1988.

40. Egeland, B., Jacobvitz, D., & Sroufe, L. A... Breaking the cycle of abuse. *Child Development*, 59, 1080-1088. Feeney, J., & Noller, P. (1996) Adult attachment. Thousand Oaks, CA: Sage, 1988).

Chapter 6
Integration vs. Defensively Split Off

We are born inherently vulnerable and totally dependent on caregivers for food, safety, and regulation, thus making an infant's attachment—bonding—to one or more caregivers critical for physical *and* emotional survival (1). Because the infant *must* attach, the infant adapts—for better or for worse—to the needs and vulnerabilities of the caregiver. Infants integrate behaviors, feelings, and desires that can be contained within the caregiver relationship, but they defensively exclude, dissociate, and disown behaviors that threaten the attachment bond (2). When caregivers lack the capacity to help children feel safe, loved, lovable, and validated for their uniqueness, substance abuse may then serve the defenses these children adopt.

During early years of life, personality and uniqueness blossom within the space created by the relationship between children and caregivers. Infants experience the stomach pains of hunger and cry out to be fed, and if caregivers respond with food, then children learn they can trust their biological experiences and emotions, along with their power to cry out for help and trust that help will be provided. Over time, when attuned caregivers respond predictably, consistently, and warmly, a sense of trust in self and others builds.

For example, a child might want to be physically close, held, and touched in play or in pleasure and comforting. If caregivers have the capacity to meet these needs, this reinforces children's sense of self-trust. From infancy they begin to integrate the notion that it is okay to approach others to have their needs met. In addition, children learn to recognize both their own needs and what others offer to meet those needs. This ongoing stream of information and feedback are integrated into the attachment relationship.

This process becomes even more sophisticated as children develop a broader range of needs, interests, and personality traits. Their attachments then play out in behavior: a curious child becomes interested in something and needs a parent with the capacity to engage with her, or a child becomes distressed or sad and needs a consistently warm, attuned caregiver to sooth him. We see this process throughout early development as children discover their unique interests, traits, and gifts. Children might be artistic, prone to intellectual pursuits, emotionally sensitive, relationally oriented, mechanically inclined, and/or right- or left-brain dominant. The more caregivers have the capacity to meet, validate, and attune to these needs, the more likely it is that those traits and gifts will be integrated into the self, and children then learn that it is safe to be who they are.

When validated, children recognize and honor their own needs, experiences, and interests. In addition, they build an ability to recognize others who are affirming, soothing, stimulating, and regulating, which in turn, allows children to feel safe in approaching others and forming relationships to regulate their needs and emotional states.

Attachment is not a static concept, but rather involves integrating experiences, which then form children's response to both internal and external processes. This integration process determines the kinds of attitudes and beliefs that develop.

They can:

Integrate a consistent sense that their needs and traits will be warmly acknowledged and met by caregivers, or split off from the parts of themselves they perceive are unacceptable to caregivers and others.

Developing the bond, along with the process of integration, is important for general wellbeing (3), but it also builds the template and expectation for all relationships throughout life (4). Beginning in infancy, children mentally represent their attachment figures and construct ideas and expectations for relationships with both these original figures and others. As previously discussed, Bowlby called this the internal working model—IWM—of attachment. While still in infancy a child internalizes patterns of relating to people, generally the parents, and forms ideas about ways to relate to others based on these representations (5). These representations also are thought of as the underlying structure that shapes the nature of sensation, perception, memory, feeling, thought, and behavior, and are likely to become consolidated as personality and/or personality disorders. In other words, children understand their range of relationships based on early interactions with caregivers, which they have internalized and organized (6). Each attachment relationship shapes the child's mental schema, which then shapes expectations for future relationships and interactions.

In the first 18 months of life, the brain is blooming and pruning billions of neurons. At this stage of neurological development, the brain is right-hemisphere dominant (7). In addition, we have twice as many neurons in the brain during the first year of life than we do as adults. During this early stage of development, the brain builds neural networks that serve as memory, representations, and routes to process the flow of information both from the body and the external environment.

To some degree, genetic inheritance is a predetermined blueprint of neurobiology; however, the environment is responsible for blooming and pruning neurons and forming neural networks. Moreover, during the period of right-hemisphere dominance, which is an experience-dependent stage of brain development, these neural networks shape what we now know to be our unconscious. The right hemisphere of the brain involves creativity and the development of language, visual perception, patterns, and impressions. In these early years, impressions and perceptions are not guided by capacities for reason and logic, which later attempt to explain behavior and allow us to understand and interpret the nuances and complexity of relationships. During our first 18 months, within the regions of the right brain, we build a significant piece of the way we see ourselves, how we feel about ourselves, approach or avoid others, and regulate affective states, which we then play out unconsciously in our daily lives (8) (9) (10).

To some degree, the explanation of the neurological process, the blooming and pruning of neurons, matches Bowlby's previous statement: *Those behaviors, feelings, desires which can be contained in the relationship of the infant to the caregiver will be integrated by the infant; those that threaten the attachment bond will be defensively excluded, dissociated, disowned* (11). Perhaps without knowing it at the time, Bowlby used psychological language to describe the biological development of neural networks and blooming and pruning of neurons, through which personality, affect regulation, and the mind emerges and gets structured.

Unfortunately, not all caregivers have a broad capacity to nurture their child's blossoming self and the development of a favorable IWM. When caregivers do not respond to a child's needs or the response is inconsistent, this impedes development of a positive sense of self and internal regulatory systems. Instead, a child may learn to both mistrust internal experiences and mistrust others as a resource for co-regulation. Sadly, children in negative or inconsistent circumstances often split off from aspects of themselves and mistrust others. Further, they overly rely on themselves and avoidance for regulation.

A Word about Attachment Theory

Attachment theory developed in the context of certain assumptions about gender roles, including the purported differences between the ways in which mothers and fathers relate to and bond with children during infancy and early childhood. We often talk about the critical importance of the infant's bond with a primary caregiver, the assumption being that in infancy the primary caregiver is the mother. Someone else takes over only if the mother is absent or unable to be the primary caregiver. Theories about attachment then grew from this assumption and have not taken into account the changes in the lives of women over the past few decades or the desire on the part of many fathers to be involved with their children in the early months and years. However, the literature about attachment has not changed much, so when examining insecure attachment and developmental histories it is usually the mother to whom we turn for information. We still assume that whether she works or stays home for the first months or years of a child's life, the mother is the primary caregiver. Even research that examines daycare, for example, assumes that a nanny or group daycare settings act as a stand-in or substitute for the mother, as opposed to a stand-in for both parents.

Available case studies, including the two presented below, reflect these older assumptions. In one case, the mother, a professional woman, is married, but the passive father had no significant role during the child's infancy. In the other case, the mother, a product of inadequate parenting herself, is a single mother raising her child alone. In both cases, the mothers assumed responsibility for the problems with their children. Ask any mother of grown children, and she'll likely tell you that no matter how society changes, the mothers are blamed by society for most of the problems with the children. (Nowadays, absent fathers are feeling the blame, too.)

In the first case study, the present, but passive and distant father says little and does not shoulder blame for being uninvolved and incapable of attunement; in the second case study the father was not around to question, let alone to enlist in helping his child. In both situations I discuss, the mothers were the only caregivers for their infants until these women returned to work. Both fit the models studied in attachment literature to date in which the burden of childcare was placed on the mothers. These mothers had the additional responsibility to partially or fully financially support their families.

We cannot say how either of the children discussed below would have fared in infancy and early childhood if a father or grandparent had been either a primary or co-primary caregiver. However, with more fathers becoming actively involved with their children during infancy and early childhood, new research may reflect the more equal roles of parents in society.

Case #1: Jason (Insecure Attachment: Dismissive-Avoidant) Parents Who Avoid the Developing Self in their Child Leads to a Child Who Avoids his own Internal Self and Avoids Others: "I'm okay, you're not okay"

Fifteen-year-old Jason was a quiet, shy, and passive adolescent, but also was an original thinker and a mechanically gifted young man. Always ready to take on the challenge of fixing things others could not, Jason preferred being by himself while he worked on motorcycles, go-carts, and other creative mechanical projects in his garage. Introverted, strong-willed, and stubborn, Jason left his parents confused about how to direct him after he started sneaking out, skipping school, using drugs, and ultimately, expelled from school for selling drugs on campus. He violated every limit his parents set, and continued doing as he pleased despite his parents' attempts to implement boundaries. As an introverted, quiet person, and socially inept in many ways, using drugs served as his social lubricant; selling drugs reinforced his sense of belonging to an accepting group.

When I evaluated Jason, I was struck by his preoccupation with trying to figure out the therapeutic process in order to avoid engaging; instead, he searched for the path of least resistance out the door. With each question I asked, he became quiet as he looked away and stared at his lap, the couch, the walls, and back to his lap. He looked anywhere but at me. After these long silences, he glanced up at me as if he forgot what I asked him. When I reiterated the question, he came up with one or two word answers and started looking around the room again.

During early treatment, I thought Jason was simply expressing his resistance and frustration about being forced into counseling, hence, the passive-aggressive silence and slow, minimal responses. I believed that as counseling progressed Jason would soften up, as others do, and see our sessions as a safe place to explore his life, thus being able to grow and find relief. However, because Jason was not verbally skilled and insightful, I moved away from the typical talk therapy. Instead, we went for walks along the river or played ping-pong or checkers. However, it soon became clear that he was not actually walking or playing checkers with me, but rather, was absorbed within himself and just happened to be next to me, much as toddlers might "parallel play." In contrast with early treatment,

131

where he resisted and showed frustration through non-engagement, I now saw his lack of capacity to engage in and negotiate relationships as the result of his early childhood experiences. It accounted for what could be called "odd" social relationships.

Left brain dominant, Jason might have been viewed as anxious or depressed, or suffering from schizoid personality disorder or having Asperger's, or perhaps he was simply a very resistant teenage boy. Although I could have easily put him into those categories, those labels would have limited my understanding of Jason and did not effectively inform the direction of his treatment. To discover what he needed, I had to understand what it felt like to be Jason, including what it felt like to be Jason as a child growing up in his family. What was it like to be nurtured and guided by his father? How had he experienced his mother's affection, care-giving, love, and nurturance? Why was he avoidant of others and his own internal experiences? What purpose has his substance abuse served?

I asked Jason's parents, Patty and Rick, to meet with me so that I could gather Jason's developmental history. Patty was an educated, professional woman, who was dressed to fit her role as a university professor. She appeared assertive, but at the same time I sensed weariness. Rick, a blue-collar, hardworking contractor, came to the appointment in his work jeans and a T-shirt. Like Jason, he presented as quiet, shy, and passive. Rick wore his sunglasses during the first half of the session, as if hiding behind them for safety.

I asked Patty and Rick about what their life was like when Jason was born: stresses and supports, unexpected events, such as the deaths of friends or family or job losses. With each question, Patty first glanced at Rick to see if he wanted to answer, but he passively shrugged as if he did not care who responded or he lacked a ready answer. Patty then turned to me and answered the questions.

Perhaps she was tired, I speculated, because she was doing all of the interpersonal and emotional work in their family. When Patty answered questions about Jason's first year, she immediately looked even more tired. Then she mentioned that Jason and his older brother were only 17 months apart, so she had been exhausted by caring for an infant and a toddler.

Patty had spent much of her life climbing the academic ladder as a university professor and researcher, ultimately having her children in her mid-30s, a situation that proved more difficult than she had anticipated. Already worn out from parenting her first child, she became depressed when Jason was born.

I asked about family and community support and learned that Patty's family lived about 1500 miles away. As a private person, and admittedly socially anxious, she did not like to share her personal life with professional friends. In the early years of her children's lives, Patty received only minimal emotional support from Rick, who also did not share in the care of the two young boys. She was forced to become overly reliant on her own exhausted internal resources to cope with life's ongoing and new demands. Viewing her job as a source of emotional respite from the family demands, Patty longed to go back to work when Jason was three months old.

When I asked how she responded to Jason when he was upset or hungry, she was candid in her answer: "I know there were times when he needed soothing and I just let him cry and times he was hungry and I just didn't care to respond right away."

Jason's developmental history provides a plethora of information about the course of his development. Jason certainly carries the genes of his father's shy, quiet, and avoidant personality; Jason's receptive mirror neurons might have picked up his father's affective state and avoidant behavior and integrated this state and emotional tone into his own neural networks. I also believe more telling variables exist. In actuality, Jason grew up with tired and avoidant parents. As a result, he did not experience others as a source of consistent, warm, and predictable attunement and soothing. Rather, he experienced inconsistency at best, and more commonly, it was a place in which he received no response, leaving him to go inward and overly rely on himself to get his needs met. When turning to others, he found that they did not acknowledge and nurture his developing self and meet his dependency needs. This meant that Jason's affect regulation system never fully developed. His internal working model, his IWM, of himself and others left him feeling unworthy of nurturance and support from others. This results in mistrusting others to be sources of help to stimulate and soothe affective states.

Jason grew up believing he needed to stay out his mother's hair, and his father engaged with him only when a mechanical issue was involved. No room existed for Jason to connect to his own internal emotions; when he expressed them in his early years, he was left alone with an unregulated emotional state. With no one attuned to him, these experiences created shame and a need to be "unseen."

Over time, theses experiences were repeated, leaving Jason's opiate and dopaminergic systems contracted and unable to thrive (12) (13); however, when teens like Jason use street drugs, these neurologically deficient systems are activated to fire which creates a state of balance and relief. Moreover, because others did not attune to his emotional states, Jason was left believing: *Others don't feel what I feel. Because they don't feel it and only I do, then something must be wrong with me.*

Jason's expression of affective states did not promote attachment. Instead, he seemed to be a source of his mother's stress, which led him to think he had to disown his internal experiences and distrust them when he felt these experiences physically and mentally. It became clear that his father, Rick, lacked the capacity to attune, and his passivity indicated a missing component in Rick's own development that left him unable to connect with his own internal processes and emotions.

Consequently, Jason had learned not to trust others as a source of support, soothing, and safety. Because his affect regulation system was not fully built, he had a limited range of affect and limited capacity to cope emotionally (14). His personality was narrow, inwardly turned, and brittle because of his parents' lack of capacity to nurture and develop their son's full range of self in his early years.

Finally, Jason learned that relief came from avoidance and over-reliance on himself in order to get his needs met. As a teen he found that street drugs and alcohol reliably and consistently served to medicate his emotional states. Furthermore, his drug dealer and drug culture responded to him every time he called out to them.

As stated earlier, caregivers with a limited capacity to nurture their children's developing self can lead children to split off from critical parts of the self. They suffer from insecure attachment and avoidance, but they may also take on characteristics of another insecure attachment type, such as the anxious-preoccupied children. These children effectively become the caregiver and must attune to their parents' emotional state and needs.

Case Study #2: Sarah (Insecure Attachment: Anxious-Preoccupied-Hyper-vigilant)

A Child Who Must Attune to the Caregiver and Loses her Self in her Preoccupation With Others' Emotional States: Codependency: "I'm not okay, you're okay"

Fashionably dressed, but anxious and depressed, Sarah was a 19-year-old straight-A college student with a passion for snowboarding when she was not busy studying, volunteering in the community, and tutoring the youth in her church. In other words, Sarah appeared to be quiet, respectful, non-confrontational, and compliant—overall, the perfect kid, student, and member of her community and church. Referred to my program from the psychiatric hospital where she had been hospitalized for a week, Sarah had stopped eating and had begun cutting her arms, thus leaving self-inflicting wounds. During that hospitalization her psychiatrist also discovered that she had a history of using vicodin, marijuana, alcohol, and Ecstasy.

Sarah had been using drugs on and off for five years, although her mother had just discovered she was using. During our initial evaluation with Sarah and her mother, Kate, I was struck by how quiet and withdrawn Kate appeared, as if we were in the same office, but she was actually somewhere else.

"Kate, can you tell me a little bit about what is going on for you right now?" I asked in a gentle voice.

As I asked the question, Kate became withdrawn and her head and upper body collapsed forward, allowing her to hide her face in her lap as she began to cry.

136

"It's all my fault that she's using drugs," Kate said. "I'm not a good enough mother for Sarah. Her father was never in the picture and I tried to do it all myself. I never knew that she was depressed or cutting herself. I'm overwhelmed, so depressed and confused."

I realized immediately what just occurred. We had started out focusing on exploring and understanding Sarah's issues and needs, but within minutes, the focus shifted to containing Kate's emotional state. This likely had been happening in their home for years. I then turned to Sarah. "Can you talk a little bit about what's going on for you right now?"

In a soft voice, Sarah said, "I don't know..."
I then said, "You look like you might be feeling depressed or sad."

She lifted her shoulders in a helpless shrug. "My mom is depressed and that makes me depressed."

To the world, Sarah appeared as the perfect girl—nice looking, excelling academically, giving back to her community, and overall, hard working. However, underneath her "I am doing great" veneer she struggled with feeling depressed, empty, exhausted, and alone. Like most experienced clinicians, I knew that diagnoses of depression, anxiety, or a substance use disorder by themselves would not be adequate to help me to understand Sarah. These diagnoses would not allow me to fully gain insights into her development, how her mind works, and the reasons for her anxiety and depression, along with her drug use. I needed a developmental history to understand her and help her feel understood.

When I met with Kate alone she described growing up with an alcoholic mother and abusive father as "hell." With a mixture of sadness and anger, Kate told me that she hated her father and referred to her mother as a bitch. "I worked my ass off to get out of that life and leave it behind me," she said with a defiant tone, "and I don't ever want to see them or revisit those memories again."

137

I asked how she thought her childhood influenced her development and the way she interacts with Sarah, and she instantly looked deflated and defeated, but just as quickly began crying in a desperate, animated way. From this hypo-manic place she kept talking about how hard she had worked to give Sarah what she needed. During the interview I observed her complete exhaustion. It took considerable energy to contain her emotions—it was always a fight, always a struggle, yet the emotions continued to hijack her behavior in extreme ways.

Kate also had a history alcohol and marijuana abuse, but she thought she'd hidden it well from Sarah. "Sarah is the love of my life," she said. "Since the day she was born, we would cuddle and she was the one thing that made me happy. I was severely depressed for the first year of her life, and Sarah was and still is my teddy bear."

Later that week, I met with Sarah so I could gain a better understanding of her childhood. Right away, she mentioned that her mom had always been depressed, moody, and unpredictable, which led to Sarah's constant fear that her mother might leave or hurt herself. According to Sarah, Kate becomes angry when she drinks, although she does not hit Sarah. Still, these moods and angry talk frighten Sarah, making it impossible to relax when her mom is upset. As Sarah had said before, when her mom is depressed, she is depressed, too.

"With such an intense connection to your mother's inconsistent moods, how are you able to do so well in school," I asked, "and find time to help out in the community and at your church?"

"I feel alone at home," Sarah replied. "My mom doesn't understand how depressed I've been, but when I do well in school and in my activities, it makes her happy. It puts a smile on her face and other people give me a lot of love for what I do."

With Jason, the caregivers lacked the capacity to help him reach his full range of self, which damaged his development. In Sarah's case, the full range of her developing self was not only unmet, but she had to attune to her mother's emotional needs as well. This led to her preoccupation with her mother's moods in the moment, while also anticipating the moods to come. Hyper-vigilance, needed at times for emotional survival, was repeated so often that over time it became more of a state of mind than a trait. She built her life around doing what others needed or wanted her to do. Whereas the avoidant-dismissive person is hyper-vigilant, as if it is not safe to rest, Sarah, with what Mary Main would classify as insecure-anxious-preoccupied attachment, expended a great deal of psychic and emotional energy to constantly scan the environment and ensure it was emotionally safe to meet others' needs and expectations. Over time, this outflow of energy left her empty, tired, and depressed.

Sarah ended up caring for and fixing her mother's emotional state so that Kate could "return the favor" and take care of Sarah's emotional state, or to put it another way, Sarah's internal dialogue was "I need to fix you so that you can fix me." This dynamic trapped and exhausted Sarah; ultimately, it damaged her affect regulation development and gave her a tattered sense of self. This left her vulnerable to peer pressure and subsequent drug abuse. Her drug use served her need to relax and for once, let go of expectations to please others.

When immersed in the drug culture, Sarah experienced others emotionally giving to her rather than taking. Sarah also met more and more people in the drug culture and spent time at their parties and gatherings. Consequently, this emotional and social attachment to the drug culture became part of her hook to drugs. The drugs were intoxicating and soothing; the drug culture came close to meeting her interpersonal needs. This setup proved to be the most significant challenge in addressing the addiction

139

part of her treatment. She was enmeshed with her drug using friends, and despite recognizing how damaging they were for her, she resisted letting go of that part of the experience. It was within that culture that she was allowed the emotional freedom not to get an "A" in every class or be involved in community, nor was she expected to fix others' emotional states in order to find approval, acceptance, and belonging.

As previously described, a child experiences arrested development when caregivers have limited capacity to connect, validate, nurture, and respond to the full range of their child's blossoming self. Lacking consistent, responsive attunement, a child may split off from those aspects of the self that the caregiver is unable to help develop. In the concept of good fit/bad fit, when the parent can attune or match a child in temperament and learning styles, there's a good fit that serves positive development. However, when caregivers lack the capacity to attune or express emotion, then a good fit is not achieved. In these situations, developing children might split off from—disown—parts of themselves that are not within their caregivers' ability to match.

Looking at the above examples, it also appears that insecure attachment can be a trans-generational issue. In other words, children might adopt the attachment inadequacies of the parents.

Family History of Attachment

"It is only through exploring the mind of the other that the child develops full appreciation of the nature of mental states" (15).

Parents can have good or bad childhoods, and they inevitably bring these experiences to their own parenting experiences. For parents with insecure attachment issues, the key to changing the patterns depends on their ability to reflect on the family dynamic and make sense of it. Although secure attachment may be a key facilitator of reflective capacity (16), it is not the final word; reflective capacity can be developed well beyond childhood and adolescence. Parents (of all backgrounds) high in reflective capacity are more likely to promote secure attachment in a child.

Chapter 6: Notes

1. Wallin J.D. *Attachment in Psychotherapy* (The Guilford Press, 2007).

2. Wallin J. D. (2007).

3. Kreppner, K., Ullrich, M. (1998). Talk to mom and dad and listen to what is in between: A differential approach to family communication and its impact on adolescent development. In M. Hoffer, J. Youniss, & P. Noack (Eds.), *Verbal interaction and development in families with adolescents* (pp. 83-108). Westport, CT: Ablex Publishing.

4. Waters, E., Merrick, S., Treboux, D., Crowell, J., & Albersheim, L. (2000). Attachment security in infancy and early adulthood: A twenty-year longitudinal study. *Child Development, 71*, 684-689.

5. Bowlby, J. (1988). "The Role of Attachment in Personality Development" (from *A Secure Base: Parent-Child Attachment and Healthy Human Development* [Basic], Lecture 7, pp. 119-136).

6. Laursen, B., & Collins, W. A. (2004). Parent-child communication during adolescence. In A. L. Vangelistsi (Ed.), *Handbook of family communication* (pp. 333-348). Mahwah, NJ: Lawrence Erlbaum Associates.

7. Cozolino. *The Neuroscience of Human Relationships: Attachment and the Developing Social Brain.* (W.W. Norton & Company, 2006).

8. Schore, A.N. *Affect Dysregulation and Disorders of the Self.* (New York: W.W. Norton, 2003).

9. Siegel, D. J. *The Developing Mind* (The Guilford Press, 1999).

10. Cozolino (2006).

11. Wallin J. D. (2007).

12. Seigel, D.J. (1999).

13. Schore, A.N. (2003).

14. Schore, A.N. (2003).

15. Hegel, G. *The Phenomenology of Spirit.* (Oxford: Oxford University Press, 1807).

16. Fonagy, P., Steele, M., Steele, H., Leigh, T., Kennedy, R., Mattoon, G., & Target, M. (1995a). Attachment, the reflective self, and borderline states: The predictive specificity of the Adult Attachment Interview and pathological emotional development. In S. Goldberg, R. Muir, & J. Kerr (Eds.), *Attachment theory: Social, developmental and clinical perspectives* (pp. 233-278). New York: Analytic Press.

Chapter 7
The Neurobiology of Attachment
Written by Claude Arnett, MD

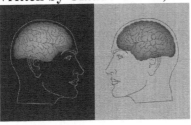

John Bowlby, a British psychologist and psychoanalyst, practiced and conducted research in the mid-twentieth century and defined attachment as "the enduring bond between a caregiver and a child." Attachment between an infant and a caregiver is like an invisible umbilical cord that nourishes the infant's growth and development after the physical cord has been cut. This lifeblood connection is most critical during a child's first three years, when 70% of brain growth occurs, and then up to age six when 90% of the structural and functional architecture of the brain is complete. The final 10 percent of brain growth is accomplished in adolescence (1).

By age six, critical structures in the brain that govern attachment have been nourished and developed and children have established their basic style or processes for attachment to peers and adults other than parents. In healthy attachment these processes promote children's connections and affiliation with their school-age peer group and foster resourceful relationships with key adults as these growing kids move through their school years. Although another critical period of brain growth occurs in adolescence, much of the process of that growth during the teen years will be determined by the structures and processes that were formed in early childhood and honed during the middle childhood years. Healthy attachment is a critical foundation that bestows the gift of relatedness. The ability to form and negotiate relationships as a child, a teen, and an adult is a strong predictor of physical and emotional wellbeing, along with the ability to form a diverse and reliable support network of family, friends, intimates, coworkers, and acquaintances (2) (3) (4).

The Path to Healthy Attachment

Attachment structures and processes develop through the moment-to-moment interaction with attuned caregivers. These incremental experiences build the brain structures in the front of the brain, which are critical to processing and regulating perception, emotion, thought, and planned behavior essential to negotiating relationships. Critical periods or windows of development exist in which key structures are nourished and their processes put into motion. We can understand each of these critical windows of opportunity and see how the moment-to-moment interactions with caregivers influence maturation of these brain structures.

It is important that we understand the critical systems of seeking, approach, and avoidance.

- The seeking system, *dopamine* (DA) based, is the alarm bell that tells us we need to pay attention to something.
- The approach system, *norepinephrine* (NE) based, tells us it is safe to move toward something.
- The avoidance system, *serotonin* (SE) based, tells us something is unsafe and to move away.
- The *endorphin* system delivers the reward and relaxation from the tension developed when these systems fire.

These four systems intersect, conflict, and negotiate to build brain structures within the amygdala, anterior cingulate, orbito-frontal cortex, prefrontal cortex, and pre-motor cortex, areas of the brain critical to regulating perception, arousal, emotion, thought, and action. These neurochemical systems and neurological structures are the building blocks of personality and relatedness. Balance in these systems and structures then creates balance in perception, emotion, thought, and action, which we then call a "well-balanced person," or one who is "easy to relate to."

The critical periods of structure-building are fueled by the brain's primary neurotransmitters: dopamine, norepinephrine, and serotonin, which flow like converging rivers into the area of development.

Dopamine (DA) is the central neurochemical in what Panskepp called the seeking system (5). It provides the initial stimulation and excitement for activity and thought to set the tone for intensity. Those who are naturally restless and intense have a high level of dopamine and high tone in the seeking system. Those who are naturally relaxed and low key have low dopamine and low tone in the seeking system.

Serotonin (SE), the largest of the three systems, is the primary neurochemical in the fear or caution system. It provides restraint and retreat from dangerous stimuli, or avoidance. Individuals high in serotonin are more naturally fearful and cautious; they avoid conflict and are less likely to take risks, and are more likely to have fearful emotions and thoughts and restrained behavior. Those low in serotonin are more likely to abandon caution and be attracted to risk, along with being impulsive and often aggressive.

Norepinephrine (NE) is the primary neurochemical in the aggression or approach system. It provides excitement and motivation toward acquiring what an individual needs. Those high in NE are likely to be aggressive, active, risk-taking, and competitive, with a strong appetite for life. They do not mind conflict and perhaps even seek it, and they likely feel confident and have confident thoughts. In short, they revel in engagement.

147

Those low in NE are more likely passive and lack confidence. They tend to wait for events to unfold rather than acting as the movers and shakers.

The three primary neurochemicals form the basis of inborn temperament and set the stage for interaction with caregivers and the development of the governing structures of the frontal lobes. In addition, we also have endogenous opioids, or endorphins. These neurochemicals are less like streams or rivers in the mind, and more like small marshy areas that develop around and nourish streams. They are critical to rewarding the growth and development of the three primary systems and structures. The systems in action can play as follows: a child's internal hunger pang signals an internal alarm and desire to eat which is the DA (desire) system firing. Then the child approaches the caregiver to seek food which is the NE (energy to approach) system now firing. During the approach, the child then scans the energy and expression of her caregiver to make sure that it is safe and she is not frustrating her caregiver which is the firing of the SE (caution) system. The child then sees she is not a burden; it is safe to approach and eat, and then the opiate system fires, which reinforces the development of the other systems as well as trust vs. mistrust and approach vs. avoidance.

Inside the Frontal Lobes

The governing structures of the frontal lobes (6) (7) are the:

- *amygdala*, which matures in the first two months of life;
- *anterior cingulated* (AC), which matures in the first two to nine months;
- *orbital-frontal cortex* (OFC), which matures from nine to 24 months;
- *prefrontal cortex* (PFC), which matures from 24-48 months, and the
- *pre-motor cortex* (PMC), which matures from 48 to 72 months.

148

An infant comes into the world with natural capacities for seeking, aggression or approach, and fear or avoidance, along with inborn capacities to develop the structures to govern them. But these capacities are absolutely dependent on the caregiving environment, or attachment. As Dan Siegel has written, "It takes adult minds to develop a child's mind" (8). The development and maturation of these systems and structures, so critical to emotional and social wellbeing, is super sensitive to the strengths and limitations of caregivers and their own regulatory systems and structures (9) (10). Here is a closer look at the key stages of attachment development.

Birth to Two Months

In the first two months infants are primarily internally focused, aroused by their internal needs for food and comfort. Mahler called this the autistic phase because infants are self-related more than other-related (11). We now know that infants have more connection to caregivers than Mahler understood, but in terms of building the neuronal systems and structures it is helpful to understand that infants are primarily concerned with their own needs. They sleep most of the time, and are awakened by discomfort, hunger, cold, or boredom. When a sleeping infant becomes uncomfortable from being hungry or cold, dopamine fires as an alarm signal and stirs primitive structures in the brainstem that lead to vocalizations that bring the caregiver.

This call-and-response mechanism is essential to survival of most species. However, these vocalizations are mitigated by approach and avoidance systems that either strengthen or subdue the vocalizations. In the prototypical situation the infant is uncomfortable, cries, and then the caregiver, distressed by the infant's cries of distress, responds quickly and calms the infant with soothing vocalizations and ministrations. As the infant calms, endorphins are released in both infant and caregiver, leading to happy and joyful feelings on the part of both. They are free from distress together, and as we typically see, the infant and caregiver interact. They might coo and play with each other and develop a capacity for joyful participation. Schore describes attachment as occurring when the caregiver can maximize pleasurable states and minimize unpleasant affective states (12).

These interactions are carried out many times a day over a period of weeks and months, allowing infants to learn that resources exist to help them with their discomfort. Since they have not become specifically focused on the caregiver, they develop a relationship to the environment, to the world, to space: "When I am uncomfortable I can call out and help is out there."

This scenario has many variables, including both the responsiveness of the caregiver and the inherent emotional intensity of the child. An intense child may call strongly and quickly stir the threshold for responsiveness in the caregiver, creating a system that is fast, taut, and reactive. A slower caregiver might frustrate the child, thus creating a more conflictual system. A mellow child might alarm one caregiver, thereby prompting responsiveness, but not engage another, which may lead to neglect. Regardless of the variables, in those first couple of months the mother/caregiver-child system develops the amygdala, the mind's first alarm system.

Input from each neurochemical system develops the amygdala's role as the initial appraisal system. Is my body okay? Should I be alarmed about something going on? Is my environment okay, or should I be alarmed about something in my environment? The amygdala sets the stage for basic feelings of readiness to approach or withdraw and an expectation of satisfaction. In healthy attachment, an attentive caregiver responds to the infant's cries and creates a predictable rhythm of need, alarm, response, and calm. Infants learn to trust the alarm of their discomfort and their needs and also trust that resources exist to relieve discomfort.

Two amygdalae exist, one right, the other left. In general, the right-side structures are focused inward and the left-side structures are focused outward, so the right amygdala appraises threat from the inside, and the left amygdala appraises threat from the outside. Normal growth and development of those structures foster healthy appraisal of both internal needs and external resources. Put another way, this development begins what Erik Erikson called the development of trust: "I can feel my needs, I can call out, I will be responded to in a way that helps me fulfill my needs and feel better" (13).

The mother (or the primary caregiver) and infant are a system. Infants develop their foundational systems and structures in concert with their mothers' established systems and structures. Healthy, loving attachment between a mother/caregiver and a child is a kind of glue that fosters engagement. It joins experiences on the outside with the caregiver and the environment, and also to the infant's internal world of needs and resources.

Healthy attachment is joyful, flexible, and dynamic. Mothers experience their infants as separate, but connected, with needs, but also as resourceful. A kind of dance develops where mothers and infants learn each other's rhythms and capacities and they learn to stimulate, support, and surprise each other. This experience between mothers and children develops systems of expectation, perception, and response. Hungry infants cry, first low and complaining, then louder and more insistently. Mothers dance in when their experience of the child's distress has reached a threshold of responsiveness. They attend to their infants' needs lovingly, warmly and both mother and child calm.

This systemic excitement and relief is the attachment system and it yokes the child to the caregiver, to themselves, and

151

to the world around them. Mothers have experienced seeking (dopamine), approach (norepinephrine), avoidance (serotonin), and satisfaction (endorphins). These neurochemical systems interact in the hierarchical structures of the mind (amygdala, AC, OFC, PFC, PMC) and are the resources mothers bring to develop those systems and structures in their infants.

These early systems are specific to mothering. For example, Schore demonstrated under functional MRI that the amygdala fires in mothers of two month old infants just as the infant is developing and maturing that structure (14). Fathers in the same experiment showed firing at the level of the anterior cingulate, one structure removed. The mothers are alarmed and in true synchrony with their infants, but fathers provide a critical perspective of support and containment.

Some might say, fathers are "out of it," as men are generally caricatured, but just as the mother-infant is a system, the mother-father is a system, and the father's role is to keep a larger perspective and to attend to the larger circle of involvement that protects the mother-infant system. The father also provides the role of striving for the next level for the infant and the system. Let's say that a two-month-old infant cries in alarm, but the parents are engaged in a much-needed romantic moment. The mother becomes alarmed and wants to immediately respond to the infant, but the father says, "She/he can wait just a minute." The father is not as alarmed, his amygdala not as engaged, but his response pulls the system toward the next level of complexity. The father, by delaying the mother's response, pulls the infant of out of alarm and reaction toward the anterior cingulate. The development of the AC heralds Mahler's stage of symbiosis, what we generally think of as loving attachment and more mutual engagement and responsiveness.

This brings us to the issue of "fit." How well do mothers' resources fit with their infants' needs and capacities? Interesting

152

studies demonstrate the importance of maternal-child "fit." Schore (15) describes a procedure where infant Rhesus monkeys are made to be low in serotonin and, therefore, overly aggressive and impulsive; another group of infant monkeys were made to be high in serotonin, making them fearful and clingy. When paired with normal rhesus mothers, these infants do not do well. The overly aggressive monkeys are killed or driven from the troop; the overly anxious monkeys are dependent and unproductive, and often are abandoned or they function marginally within the troop. However, when paired with Rhesus "super-caretaker" monkeys, who are exquisitely sensitive, patient, and responsive to their young, the aggressive monkeys become leaders and the fearful monkeys become super-caretakers.

Other studies (16) (17) (18) (19) (20) have shown that genetically bred uptight/anxious monkeys will drink alcohol as if to self-medicate. Further, monkeys genetically bred to be low in the serotonin metabolite 5-Hydroxyindoleacetic acid (5-HIAA) were impulsive, aggressive, and did not learn from consequences. When placed in a so-called Happy Hour situation, they would drink like binge drinkers. However, when these genetically-controlled monkeys were cross-fostered and raised by nurturing caregivers they drank less than the normal rhesus monkeys.

Infants come into the world with endowments that sensitive mothers/caretakers must learn to navigate and negotiate. The more extreme an infant's natural temperament, the more sensitive, patient, flexible, and responsive the caretaker must be. When this fit works well, infants are connected to their internal and external resources in a flexible and dynamic way. These infants are able to negotiate what resources they can trust, both in themselves and in others, which forms the foundation of functioning with a healthy feeling of trust. This trust supports the development of secure attachment. In Transactional Analysis secure attachment is described as: *You're okay, I'm okay.*

More realistically, it is a series of healthy evaluations:
Are you okay? Am I okay?
Yes, you are okay in these ways, not so in these other ways,
but that is okay.
I am okay in these ways, not so in these other ways, but that is okay.

Two to Nine Months

At two months, infants develop the social smile, which is no longer a reflexive grimace, but a smile in recognition of the caregiver. This begins the period that Margaret Mahler called the Symbiotic period, where mothers and infants are locked into a feeling of joyful symbiosis (21). This is the period of inside-to-inside connection, in which mothers and infants come to know each other. Experiments with eye gaze between mothers and infants have shown the delicate dance of excitement and rest when they look into each others' eyes.

In one session the mother and infant are delightedly seeing each other; the infant coos and squirms and the mother mirrors the excitement. Then the infant turns away, the mother follows suit, and both calm and rest, only to resume their connection and excitement a few moments later. Alan Schore (22) says this period develops the anterior cingulate, a structure central to attachment and seeking, in which eye gaze and mobilization are linked. Daniel Stern (23) describes this healthy attachment process in terms of shared experiences: shared attention, emotion, and intention. Here, infants and mothers share their interest and attention with each other, thus sharing joy, apprehension, their brief separation followed by their reunion. These powerful first experiences of emotion and connection are building blocks that support attachment. In addition to attention and emotion, mothers and infants begin to know one another, to experience each others' rhythms, and along with that, build expectations of intention.

154

These first steps toward shared intention join infants and mothers in a joint enterprise, even if it is small and brief. For example, while being held, an infant might take hold of her necklace and mouths it. They have created a set of shared expectations that directs each of their behaviors and pleases both. These day-to-day, moment-to-moment interactions stimulate the input of NE, 5-HT (serotonin receptors), DA, and opioids into the AC, thereby fostering this structure's growth and development.

A healthy anterior cingulate leads to a focus on a target of interest and movement toward it or away from it, depending on how the target is appraised. This means that interactions between mothers and infants lead healthy adults to notice someone, make an appraisal of safe or unsafe, and move toward or away from that person.

Again, the right AC receives information about the body and readies it for movement. The left receives information about the attachment figure and initiates the movements of approach or withdrawal. This coordination between inside and outside experiences is critical to healthy functioning. This is the process by which infants learn to match inside experiences of need and safety to movements of approach and inside experiences of fear to movements of avoidance. This can be as simple as infants feeling safe and warm in the mother's lap, relaxing the back muscles and using the muscles in the front of the spine to curl around the mother's body. Or, the infant might feel uncomfortable, fearful, or angry, and then contract the muscles of the back to arch away from the mother. This move generally leads to an infant being placed somewhere else, such as in a bed or in someone else's arms.

In the coordination of neurochemical systems, we can connect a sense of safety and approach with NE, which has greater input into the right AC, and the feeling of fear and avoidance with the left AC. In nature, avoiding damaging experiences is more important than capitalizing on positive experiences. This means that the left AC is dominant over the right until the right has reached a threshold of need that leads to overriding the left. Most of us would rather pass up a meal if we might have to fight for it and be injured in the process. We prefer to wait for another opportunity to eat a meal that involves less risk. Of course, the hungrier we are the more risk we will endure to get our need met.

In healthy development, the function of the left and right AC results in an internal experience of need and readiness for action, which is inhibited by an appraisal of the situation. At around seven to nine months infants develop stranger anxiety. They will reach for and are comfortable with their primary caregiver, but cry and try to get away from others, even people they previously allowed to hold them. This demonstrates maturation of the structures that perform critical evaluations. Essentially the infant is saying: "I want to be held by my mommy and only my mommy. You are not my mommy! I am safe and happy with my mommy and no one else." Attachment is specific, not general.

Nine Months to 24 Months

Development is multi-systemic; each system interacts with the others to build structures with greater complexity and wider connectivity. As the infant learns to more clearly differentiate between mommy/caregiver and everyone else, they also are developing greater mobility, allowing them to move toward or away from people who they see and process as safe or unsafe. With more independent movement, the orbito-frontal cortex is starting to mature. Input from DA, NE, 5-HT, and the endorphins build toddlers' capacity to learn from their own mistakes. Rather than being passive and having to react to being picked up by someone they evaluate as safe or unsafe, they independently move toward or away. The orbito-frontal cortex processes the results of those decisions. "Ah, this person feels good, good job crawling into this lap," or, "Oh, this person is scary, so squirm and struggle to get away."

Though conducted in neurochemicals, not words, this is a dialogue primarily with the self. Margaret Mahler (24) called this stage of development Rapprochement, or separation-individuation, in which toddlers gain a sense of mastery over their bodies, and they experience a great deal of excitement and curiosity. The OFC is critical to processing the excitement and the results of approach or avoidance behavior.

During the first two months of life (Mahler's autistic or "self-absorbed" stage), the infant is self-oriented. During the next phase of development, 2-9 months, Mahler's Symbiotic or "merged" stage, the infant is more focused on the mother. The toddler period, Mahler's Separation-Individuation stage, is a return to concern about and development of the self.

In addition to gaining mastery over mobility, the toddler period is an intense time of learning to manage the risks and benefits of movement toward or away from people and objects of interest. Like all developmental processes, Separation-Individuation progresses incrementally in the day-to-day interactions with the caregiver. As with other stages, it is significantly influenced by inborn temperament.

Toddlers are organized around the mother/caregiver as a safe base. Assertive, adventurous toddlers venture away from their safe base and toward objects of interest. Mothers and other caregivers often chase after toddlers in order to reel them back from excessive risk. They caution them by saying no, and then anchor them by holding their hands and telling them to stay close by. Fearful, shy, risk-averse toddlers can be clingy, watching the world from the mother's lap or they walk a few steps toward objects of interest, but then hurry back to the safety of the mother. Mothers often encourage shy, cautious toddlers while at the same time anchoring them with their reassuring presence. These moment-to-moment interactions occur many times per day, weaving these threads into a fabric of trust and shared experience. This is much like the dance between mother and infant, but on a wider, more mobile stage.

This lengthening "leash" between toddlers and the primary caregiver builds the toddler's confidence and security, which means engaging in a wider, more challenging circle of stimulation. The mother's attunement to the toddler's needs for restraint and/or encouragement builds critical balance in the structures that govern risk-taking. This also regulates excitement, fear or caution, disappointment and frustration, and forms the foundation of the self interacting with the world.

Here again, the OFC has right and left side functions. The right OFC processes the internal experience of excitement, fear, frustration, and disappointment. The left OFC processes the release of these emotional experiences into physical and vocal expressions. Children high in dopaminergic intensity and high in NE will have high tone in the right OFC. These toddlers experience a high level of internal pressure from emotion, particularly more aggressive, risk-taking emotions. If equally balanced in serotonin and a sense that the impulses toward movement and vocalization might be dangerous, we see an intense conflict between "go" and "stop."

Small changes in the internal environment, like being hungry, tired, or uncomfortable in other ways might tilt the system one way. Likewise, changes in the external environment, the arrival of a trusted caregiver, the appearance of a stranger, the recognition of an object of interest will push this conflict toward approach or avoidance. This system of taut conflict is essential to healthy development; it gives the system a broader, faster range of responsiveness, and ultimately, adaptivity. A fragile system, particularly early in this stage of development, it is prone to becoming overwhelmed and breaking down, often resulting in temper tantrums. More aggressive children have more prominent, classic tantrums. Shy youth are more likely to use "hostile withdrawal," meaning they retreat into angry, mute, and uncooperative states.

Temper tantrums are common during the toddler period and are central in developing the internal experience and management of emotion. Feeling overly restrained or overly pushed by internal or external forces brings about the sense of being overwhelmed. Toddlers then cry or throw themselves on the floor. They might bite themselves, run and hide, or otherwise shut down and refuse to talk or move. Naturally aggressive children tend to have more classic tantrums; tantrums among more cautious children tend might be less obvious, but these children become more avoidant, and deeply experience shame and the pressing need to hide and shut down. Caregivers are critical in helping to manage these experiences. An unsafe level of aggression needs restraint and calming, but excessive shame and avoidance needs to be handled, too, with the toddlers coaxed into acceptance and soothing.

Toddlers express intense emotion with their bodies and words during tantrums, but generally without real risk of harm, and they are an important developmental experience. These young children experience and express intense emotion, but it is contained within the self. The typical tantrum occurs when mothers or caregivers say no to a request (candy in the supermarket, for example) and the toddler whines and makes another request, followed with another that shows increasing frustration. Finally overwhelmed, the "fit" begins. Toddlers typically pull on the caregiver, sit down or throw themselves on the floor and begin kicking and screaming.

Most parents interrupt this kind of episode and remove the child from the public place. However, in private the tantrum often plays out, ending with the toddlers becoming worn out, finally willing to accept comfort over the disappointment of not getting what they want. These repetitive experiences stretch the toddler's capacity for managing stimulation. They build structures enabling children to experience intense emotion without feeling overwhelmed. Children also develop skills for self-soothing or seeking external resources for soothing when challenging emotions arise.

This period of nine to 24 months (and up to 36 months, allowing for variation in rates of maturity) develops what Antonio Damasio calls "the emotional loop" or "the feel of what happens" (25). The emotional loop involves structures critical to processing the way we experience and manage emotion, and include: the amygdala, septal nuclei, hippocampus, nucleus accumbens, anterior cingulate, insula, and orbital-frontal cortex.

Emotional processing is differentiated from cognitive processing. Put another way, the situation represents implicit learning versus explicit learning. Implicit learning involves bodily experience of emotion, i.e., pleasurable or not pleasurable, safe or not safe. Toddlers do not decide through a thinking process, but rather, feel their way through an experience, moving forward when it feels good, drawing back when it feels unpleasant or scary. Piaget called this "sensori-motor processing," or thinking with the body, through the experience of sensation and movement (26).

The maturation of the OFC provides nuanced regulation of this "navigation-by -feel." The confidence that results from mastery of the body and navigation by feel through the world of pleasures and disappointments constructs what Erickson called *autonomy*, a balanced sense of "I can." The development and maturation of the OFC is central to this "I can" experience. The

OFC is also critical to contain emotion and for the connection to and recruitment of higher level resources, which include cognitive resources used for further processing, such as conscious decision-making and thoughtful planning.

Twenty-four to 48 months

By three-years-old, 70% of a child's structural brain growth has been accomplished. The basic connections of systems to structures have been established, along with the basic size and capacity of these structures. We can liken this to a map of a city, with most the streets laid out, and many buildings that house critical functions to manage the city are in place—the grocers, hardware stores, hospitals, the courthouse and jail, and schools. But the roads are not finished and the buildings need further development to become fully functional.

We describe neurological development as a "blooming and pruning" process. Blooming is the growth and connection of neurons that establish pathways, and pruning cuts back unproductive connections in order to conserve energy and improve efficiency. By age three, much of the initial blooming has been accomplished. Mothers or primary caregivers have fostered much of the growth of the critical pathways and structures that become the regulatory controls for emotion and close relationships. Dopaminergic systems have developed to provide a basic level of tone or intensity to approach and avoidance. Noradrenergic systems have grown to support reward for risk and resilience. Serotonin systems are maturing to reward caution and restraint and the ability to avoid harm.

Typically, the mother does much of the parenting from birth to twenty-four months. Fathers often act in supportive roles, helping out at the mother's request or stepping in when the mother is tired and overwhelmed. Much early developmental experience focuses on "mothering" as a concept, even if it is not the mother who provides support and supervision. Most early developmental interactions are experienced as mothering and develop what might be called the "mother structures," which are essentially the structures in the emotional loop. However, these structures are somewhat more complicated than bottom (pre-cortical, lower cortical) versus top (higher cortical).

Each structure that processes perception and emotion has a mirror structure, one in the right hemisphere and one in the left. In early infant development, both right and left structures are primarily influenced by "mothering experiences." But around 18 months, toddlers' increasing mobility, increasing vocalizations, and increased capacity for cognitive processing draw the father into deeper engagement. The relationship with the father adds new layers of complexity to attachment and to the parents' roles in the maturation of structures that process emotion and cognition.

Fathers typically excite toddlers; they throw them up in the air, chase them around, pick up bugs, and wrestle. Mothers often play the role of calming the over-excited pair so father and child do not get out-of-control. This intrusion of excitement into the "mothering structures" is the beginning of a child's experience of the father and of the parents as a team.

Fathers often represent progressive elements of developmental experience, the push toward risk, growth, and independence. Mothers play more of the regressive role in development and provide comforting, nurturing, the safe home to revisit and become restored. In a gross over-simplification, we can see fathers as fostering development of the noradrenergic system and the sympathetic nervous system, which governs excitement, fighting, and fleeing. We can view mothers as fostering development of the serotonin system and parasympathetic nervous system, which governs safety, rest, relaxation, and restoration. Of course, both parents foster the development of both systems, in a dizzying dance of complexity between the two during each different stage of their children's development. In this over simplification, it is noteworthy that that in the earlier stages of development, birth to 24 months, we see more development of excitement, whereas in later stages, 36 to 72 months we see more development of restraint.

At 24 to 48 months children begin to move into a wider, more complex world. They might be part of a play group, attend preschool, and develop a more cognitive relationship to experience. Words represent an important stimulus for this growth. Children experience the magic of words, such as the first nouns: mom, dad, dog, and so forth. This naming stirs the child's relationship to what is named, as if claiming and possessing, or, metaphorically planting a flag. A bit later they learn verbs, such as go, run, stay, and then sentences, "I go," "dog run," and "mom stay." Through this process children experience more deeply their relationship with others, plus the relationships of others independent of them. This sets up the stage of development that Sidney Blatt called "Mutuality" (27) (28).

Blatt thought the cycles in development of self-to-other required a stage between Erickson's Autonomy and Initiative, and Mutuality is that stage (29). It involves preschoolers' realization of the triangular attachment between themselves and their parents. Initially, it is a magical realization, "We are one big happy family," not the more reality-based competitive relationship, as described in Freud's Oedipal conflict. The preschooler becomes more attached to the father, not yet realizing that the attachment to the father is a potential threat to the relationship with the mother, or even to the relationship between the mother and father. In mutuality the preschooler has the feeling of "my daddy," "my mommy," and "me," a magical sense of "this is all mine" and "we are all doing this together."

The OFC is maturing, managing higher levels of emotional intensity and complexity. Preschoolers' joy in their own growing sense of self, in the idealized relationship with the parents, in the harmony of being a family, leads to the need to manage conflicting feelings of disappointment, nervousness, frustration, insecurity, and so forth.

The relationship with the father starts to recruit the prefrontal cortex, the right prefrontal cortex in particular, because it brings in imagination as a resource to manage discomfort. The preschooler moves from the experience of reality as sensori-motor (I am what I feel and do) to the experience of reality as pre-operational, the magical "I am what I imagine myself to be."

Freud said that preschool age children construct a central fantasy of the self: the boy as knight in shining armor who saves his mother, the girl as beautiful princess who delights her father. These fantasies then become a driving force in psychological maturation. This central fantasy, usually in the form of a picture in the mind, represents a small move from the direct attachment to the parents to attachment to the products of their own minds. And it is a critical step toward connecting the emotional loop to the cognitive loop.

When this stage goes well, the children build important foundations: attachment to the mother, the father, the family, and to their imagined self, which is an attachment to their mental constructions. These foundations are critical in managing the many challenges of the next stage of development, 48-60 months, when children reach kindergarten age.

Five-year-olds are ushered into the deep complexities of the so-called real world. The left prefrontal cortex matures and along with it, the awareness of competition and conflict, conquest and defeat. This awareness casts a nervous shadow over the idealized happy family. The left prefrontal cortex develops much more directly in relationship to the father, to the father as authority figure in particular.

In Freud's oedipal conflict, the wishful child wants the family as they wish it, my mommy, my daddy. But the father represents the reality that mommy and daddy already have a relationship, a relationship exclusive of the child in many ways. Difficult to manage, this disappointment threatens children's imagined visions as knight or princess. Reality intrudes, and dreams and wishes must yield to the realities of time, place, and limited resources. Conflict with reality is intense, and children hold on to their wishes. Fathers are strong in their insistence that the children grow up and accept their limitations in time and space and join the family in their role as the children.

In healthy families, children yield to their fathers and make a compromise: "Okay, I accept my role as a child now and the limitations inherent in that role, but I am going to grow up and be an adult like you and Mom someday and have a family of my own." This acceptance represents the full maturation of prefrontal functioning, in which children accept a sense of time and space, imagine the future, and create a compromise between the immediate reality and the hoped for future.

Strong prefrontal functioning allows children and adults to recognize the immediate context of a situation, determine what mindset and behaviors are adaptive in that context, and then conform accordingly. A strong prefrontal cortex is the proverbial "mind over matter," the development of an internalized sense of authority, which is our ability to direct our own behavior. Erickson called this Initiative, meaning that children have matured in their regulation of perception, emotion, thought, and directed behavior to the point that they can have their own sense of initiative, or the ability to make their own way.

The School-age Child

The maturation of the prefrontal cortex, and following closely, the pre-motor cortex, completes the system of pathways and structures critical to adaptive regulation of perception, emotion, thought, and behavior. At this point, the child is ready for more independence and prepared for school and school-age peer groups. Myelination, the process by which a sheath-like covering develops over neurons, represents the primary growth area in the brain for school-age children. Myelination turns the small connecting roads between structures into super highways and by orders of magnitude, increases the speed, efficiency, and complexity of the child's processing and regulating.

Interestingly, the same relational cycles that formed these pathways and structures repeat within peer groups. Children go through a "forming" stage, in which they build early trust, a basic acceptance into the group. Then we see the "storming" or autonomy-building stage, where children assert their individuality in the group. After some conflict and wrangling, a "norming" or mutuality-building stage emerges, in which the group changes and accommodates all the individuals in the group. Finally, we see a "performing" or initiative-building stage, in which the group supports its members' strengths and minimizes their weaknesses, thus forming a seamless whole, like a well-tuned orchestra playing joyously and harmoniously together.

It is critical to understand that the healthy negotiation of attachment in the first four stages of life, and building the systems and structures of regulation, are strong determinants of healthy participation in the school-age peer group. By extension, healthy attachment in the school-age peer group is a strong predictor of healthy adult adjustment.

The Adolescent Mind

Ninety percent of the structural and functional architecture of the mind is formed by age six or seven, then honed into a super-efficient processor during the school-age years when much myelination occurs. The other 10% of brain growth happens in the teen years from age twelve to twenty. As might be expected, the growth that occurs in the teenage brain follows the four cycles of growth first established in early childhood, then honed to efficiency in the school-age child. The preteen brain challenges and grows the capacity of the anterior cingulate to connect mind to body, thought to emotion. Early teens expand the capacity to manage emotion in the OFC. Middle and late teens become more focused and directed through the full maturation of the PFC and PMC.

Preteens, ages 11-13, recapitulates the attachment experience of infancy by having what Harry Stack Sullivan called, "the chum," the best friend (30). The best friend is almost always the same gender and is important for developing intense emotional bonds in a safe way and for consolidating the gender identity of the preteen child. This recapitulates Erickson's development of trust and the relationship with the mother in infancy; it is a good predictor of how this developmental experience is negotiated.

Early teens, ages 13 to 15, are responsible for the "rebellious teen" reputation. The surge of hormones, along with physical and sexual growth during this period, temporarily overwhelms the regulating structures, which were previously so dependable. Early teens, like toddlers, tend to be emotionally fragile, self absorbed, and require a delicate balance of support and restraint. Early teen groups tend to be gender-based and are the "safe place" that nourishes and restores them. The boy group and girl group are parallel. They go to the same places, have peripheral interactions, but retreat to the safety of the group to restore and process their excursions. Development as a toddler is a good predictor of the negotiation of early teen development and a more mature and complex sense of autonomy.

Middle and late teens begin to gain full control of their regulatory capacities. This allows them to tackle more complex problems in school, develop judgment to drive a car, and learn to manage intense emotions so they can explore romantic relationships and intimate encounters. Again, these are recapitulations of the development of mutuality and initiative, the same pathways and structures building bigger, faster, more complex connections and capacities. Finally, identity is consolidated, which Erickson said is the task for adolescents. They develop an attendant direction and commitment towards participation in the "real world," which means getting an education, choosing a career, finding long-term relationships, and integrating guiding values.

Preschool and kindergarten age experiences are predictors of successful navigation of the middle and late stages of adolescent development. In turn, the negotiation of adolescence is a predictor of the adult capacity to develop a network of supportive relationships and a commitment to productive participation in the community.

The Big Picture

To summarize, attachment is accomplished through attunement, and this attunement makes connections, critical connections to important relationships and between essential structures. Critical periods in development establish pathways and build structures. In healthy attachment, attunement in the relationship with the mother or mothering figures build the basic foundation for trust and autonomy and the regulatory capacities for perception and emotion. Attunement by the father in the family setting builds capacity for mutuality and for initiative, and

168

for the regulation of thought and directed behavior. These early experiences and the pathways and structures they construct represent strong predictors of later adaptation in the school-age peer group and further growth and development in the teen age years.

Evidence exists that the human mind remains plastic, but these early windows of opportunity powerfully shape the mind and significant time and resources are needed to later change what has been firmly established. A depressed and poorly attuned mother, an overbearing and critical father, psychological traumas, or unexpected losses all affect the construction of these critical pathways and structures that provide regulatory capacity and, therefore, adult adaptivity.

Much addictive behavior and psychopathology can be traced to disruptions in regulatory capacity, usually disruptions in attachment in early childhood. In turn, most of the capacity for recovery can be found in the early experiences of attunement that bring a shared sense of joy, respect, support, and hope.

Chapter 7: Notes

1. Healy, J. *Your Child's Growing Mind: A Practical Guide to Brain Development and Learning from Birth to Adolescence*. (New York: Doubleday, 1994).

2. Freeney, J., Noller, P., University of Queensland, St. Lucia, Queensland, Australia, Attachment Style as a Predictor of Adult Romantic Relationships. *Journal of Personality and Social Psychology* 1990, Vol. 58, No. 2, 281-291 American Psychological Association, Inc. 022-3514/90/SO0.75.

3. Van Ijzendoorn, M. H., Schuengel, C., & Bakermans-Kranenburg, M. J. (1999). Disorganized attachment in early childhood: Meta-analysis of precursors, concomitants, and sequelae. *Development and Psychopathology,* 11, 225-249.

4. Belsky, J., Campbell, S., Cohn, Jeffrey F., Moore, G., Instability of infant-parent attachment security. *Developmental Psychology.* 1996 Sep Vol 32(5) 921-924.

5. Panksepp, J. *Affective neuroscience: the foundations of human and animal emotions*. (Oxford University Press, 2004).

6. Schore, A.N. *Affect Dysregulation and Disorders of the Self.* (New York: W.W. Norton, 2003).

7. Krasnegor, N., Lyon, P., Goldman-Rakic, P. *Development of the prefrontal cortex: evolution, neurobiology, and behavior*. (Brookes Pub. Co., 1997).

8. Siegel, D. J. *The Developing Mind* (Guildford Press, 1999).

9. Schore, A.N. (2003).

10. Siegel, D. J. (1999).

11. Mahler, S., Pine, F., and Bergman, A. *The psychological birth of the human infant.* (New York, Basic Books, 1975).

12. Schore A. N. (2003).

13. Erikson, Erik. *Identity: Youth and Crisis.* (New York: Norton. 1968); *The Life Cycle Completed: A Review.* (New York: Norton. 1985); *Childhood and Society.* Second Edition. New York: Norton. 1963.

14. Schore, A.N. (2003).

15. Schore, A.N. (2003).

16. Champoux, M., Boyce, W. T., & Suomi, S. J. (1995). Biobehavioral comparisons between adopted and nonadopted rhesus monkey infants. Journal of Developmental Behavioral Pediatrics, 16, 6-13.

17. Higley, J. D., Suomi, S. J., & Linnoila, M. (1996). A nonhuman primate model of Type II excessive alcohol consumption? (Part 1): Low CSF 5-HIAA concentrations and diminished social competence correlate with excessive alcohol consumption. Alcoholism: Clinical and Experimental Research, 20, 629-642.

18. Higley, J. D., Suomi, S. J., & Linnoila, M. (1996). A nonhuman model of Type II alcoholism? (Part 2): Diminished social competence and excessive aggression correlates with low CSF 5-HIAA concentrations. Alcoholism: Clinical and Experimental Research, 20, 643-650.

19. Higley, J. D., Suomi, S. J., & Linnoila, M. (1997). Progress in the development of a nonhuman primate model of alcohol abuse. Journal of the Alcoholic Beverage Medical Research Foundation, 7, 67-78.

20. Fahlke, C., Lorenz, J. G., Long, J., Champoux, M., Suomi, S. J., & Higley, J. D. (2000). Rearing experiences and stress-induced plasma cortisol as early risk factors for excessive alcohol consumption in nonhuman primates. Alcoholism: Clinical and Experimental Research, 24, 644-650.

21. Mahler, M., Pine, F., and Bergman, A. *The psychological birth of the human infant.* New York, Basic Books (1975).

22. Schore, A.N. (2003).

23. Daniel Stern, *The Interpersonal World of the Infant: A View from Psychoanalysis and Developmental Psychology.* (Basic Books, 1984).

24. Mahler, M., Pine, F., Bergman, A. (1975).

25. Damsio, Antonio, *The Feeling of What Happens: Body and Emotion in the Making of Consciousness.* (Mariner Books, 1999.

26. Piaget, J... *The origins of intelligence in children.* (New York: International Universities Press, 1952).

27. Blatt, S.J. & Lerner, H.D. (1983a). Investigations on the psychoanalytic theory of object relations and object representations. In: J. Masling (Ed.), *Empirical studies of psychoanalytic theories*, Vol. 1 (pp. 189-249). Hillsdale: NJ: Analytic Press.

28. Blatt, S.J. & Shichman, S. (1983). Two primary configurations of psychopathology. *Psychoanalysis and Contemporary Thought*, 6, 187-254.

29. Blatt, S., Shichman, S. (1983).

30. Sullivan, H. S. *The Psychiatric Interview*. (New York, W.W Norton, 1970).

Chapter 8

Affect Regulation

Attachment theory is essentially a regulatory theory, and

attachment can be defined as the interactive regulation of

biological synchronicity between organisms.

Alan N. Schore, Ph.D. (1)

Teenage and young adult addicts rarely return to wellness simply by becoming drug free. Beneath their addictive disorder, we typically see a compromised affect regulation system. If drugs alone were the problem, then adolescents (and adults, too) would be well after they quit using. In treatment, then, our goals are:
- assessing where and how the drug users' capacity for affect regulation was undeveloped or arrested, and
- helping users develop their capacity for affect regulation.

Since the mid-1990s, Alan N. Schore, Ph.D. has been the prominent researcher on the link between attachment and the neurobiology of affect regulation. His work has shown that affect regulation does not spontaneously occur from DNA, but rather it is developed and is experience-dependent in the first two years of life. Affect regulation develops within a warm, consistent, and attuned parent-child dyad; neurobiologically it is developed in the right orbital prefrontal cortex. In contrast, research shows that early relational trauma and stress are growth-inhibiting in the development of regulatory corticolimbic circuits. Early trauma

175

and stress result in immature frontolimbic control systems, and an inefficient right frontal hemisphere, hence, limited capacity for affect regulation (2).

The [right] orbital frontal cortex mediates neurophysiological mechanisms integrating several domains of human experience: social relationships, the evaluation of meaning, autonoetic consciousness, response flexibility, and emotion regulation. The nonverbal social signals of eye contact, facial expression, tone of voice, and body gestures communicate the state of mind for each member of a dyad. The interactions that occur have direct effects on the emotional experience in that moment. Within the context of an attachment relationship, the child's developing mind and the structure of the child's brain will be shaped in such a way that the ability to regulate emotion in the future will be affected (3).

Based on this brain development, early relational traumas and failed attachment histories contribute to the child's inability to regulate both negative and positive affective states. During the tumult of adolescence, faulty affective capacity sets up a situation primed for substance abuse because the adaptational/regulatory resources are already taxed. In early recovery we often see affect dysregulation and suffering because the relationship to intoxication as a soothing object is taken away. Many young people feel empty, bored, anxious, and they fear they have nothing to offer in their relationships now that they do not show up to social events with drugs, which had previously acted as their way to belong. They may also believe they no longer know how to have fun, and they fear others will no longer see them as fun. As a result, they are now stuck trying to figure out what to do with this new anxiety, but also are aware that they need to continue their psychological, emotional, and relational development.

As in early childhood, when we cannot auto-regulate and must turn to others for co-regulation, teens and young adults in early recovery must relearn to turn to others for co-regulation, a safe haven, and support. However, many of these young people have a history of early relational traumas. This means that their IWM (Internal Working Model), which is neurologically hardwired into the implicit memory in the brain's right-hemisphere, sends a different message. It tells these teens that they are not loveable, valid, or worthy, and, therefore, not to trust what they feel or to turn to others for comfort and support. Turning to and trusting others are unfamiliar experiences.

Because chemical substances blunted the edges of their emotions, many teens believe that drug use has taken away most of their internal turbulence. Many newly drug-free teens I have worked with discover that rather than outgrowing issues involved with affect regulation, their drug use merely masked them. Within the 12-step community, it is said that addiction causes emotional arrest and, therefore, at the time addicts get sober, they are emotionally the age they were when they started using. That means that newly clean and sober teenagers are forced to go back and face what may have driven their addiction, i.e., their hurts, pain, sadness, anger, identity confusion, and relational insecurity.

The inability of the affect regulatory system to help teens soothe in early recovery represents a setup for relapse. These teens know that picking up the drugs will take away their emotional turmoil and they will feel better, at least temporarily. In addition, the drug culture is ready to accept them so they do not have to feel alone or socially unskilled. Generally, only the accountability being imposed by family, school, work, or probation keeps them drug free.

Those of us involved in treating adolescents and young adults, including therapists, counselors, and other support systems, such as their 12-step groups, ask them to hold onto trust and hope in order to get through early sobriety. We know that being drug free is not the same as being well. Therapists must simultaneously challenge their clients' denial, while offering the experience of validation, unconditional positive regard, and support. We do this with the hope that a healthy client-therapist relationship will rewrite the teen's IWM.

Nathan

I started treating Nathan when he was 17 years old. Tall, muscular, and quiet, he constantly scanned others to see how they were looking at him, making his insecurity transparent to most people. He studied others, and then looked at his chest, puffing it up and throwing his shoulders back. He compulsively looked in every mirror he passed, seeing what others might see. Nathan's physique was his compensation for feeling weak and inferior; it served as his armor, always there to protect himself and keep other guys intimidated and at a safe distance.

With this profile, Nathan, quiet, insecure, and afraid of others, lived inside his own mind and body, regularly working out and watching movies for escape. According to his own reports, he felt as if he took on the identity of characters in the movie. He once wanted the nickname "Snake," based on the character in the movie, "Escape from New York."

Nathan was one of the most dangerous drug users I ever worked with. He lacked the capacity to down-regulate with weightlifting, sports, relationships, and drugs. He had sustained multiple sports-related injuries, and had been thrown off many teams for "going off" when he got frustrated. His drug use was always extreme. On the same night that he would drink as much as he could, he would also use cocaine, smoke marijuana, and take a large number of pills.

When Nathan was seven, his mother put him on a plane to go live with his alcoholic dad, who then raised him. His mother made this arrangement with the airline, which saw to it that he arrived safely. However, his father never knew Nathan was arriving until the last minute, when he received a call from Nathan's mother saying, "Your son is on a plane headed to your place and will be landing in two hours. He's your responsibility now."

More out of obligation than enduring love, Nathan's father picked him up and took him home. Unfortunately, Nathan's stepmother despised him. Although not physically abusive, she was mean, often taunting him with the story of his mother's lack of love for him and her "airport" abandonment. Nathan's mother sent Christmas and birthday presents, but his stepmother gave them to her own children. Unfortunately, Nathan's father did not step in to protect him from this kind of behavior, or with the ridicule and scorn. Nathan suffered from his stepmother.

Nathan described his father as absent even when he was present, habitually drinking beer from the time he got home until the time he went to bed. Nathan longed to be loved by his parents and stepmother, but he never felt love, not even during his first two years when he was raised by both parents, who fought all the time and divorced when Nathan was two. After the divorce, his mother became preoccupied with her image and career, along with her new-found freedom. She viewed Nathan (and his father, too, prior to the divorce) as an exhausting chore that she could barley tolerate. Finally, Nathan reported experiencing his father's physical abuse, but also said he lacked any memories prior to age six.

Nathan was a young sensitive boy longing for love, family, consistency, and warmth, but found others as a source of pain and confusion. The only sense he could make from his experience led to a distorted self-image. He judged himself as ugly, dumb, boring, inadequate, unlovable, and unworthy, which left him anxious, depressed, and mistrustful of others. The negative view of himself and his emotions in relation to others led to Nathan's anger and occasional violence. He longed to be close to other people, but simultaneously viewed others as a threat to his physical and psychological wellbeing. Because Nathan judged himself and others so harshly, he focused on his deficits and failed to hear how others perceived his strengths.

Early in my work with Nathan, he went to an inpatient treatment center that focused on working with teens and young adults with dual diagnoses. Prior to his inpatient treatment, Nathan had a DUI and his father had busted Nathan for using drugs many times. In addition, an overdose led to hospitalization. After 45 days of treatment, Nathan went home drug free, with a new vocabulary to describe his emotional states. He also had learned how to own his role in relationships. After two weeks, however, Nathan's vocabulary began to regress and his motivation for change had diminished. If he were to relapse, his family and the psychiatrist were going to put him back into treatment. But in the meantime we wanted to set up as much support as possible. In addition to working with me twice a week in individual therapy and once a week in group therapy, he also attended weekly yoga, massage, art therapy, and family therapy facilitated by his psychiatrist.

This intense wraparound service provided structure and containment within a multidisciplinary team, which afforded multiple attachments to count on as resources. Nathan stayed drug free after 45 days in treatment (a relatively short treatment period), but he was still depressed, anxious, socially afraid, and overly reliant on physical fitness and his physical image to regulate his affective states and hold his tattered identity together.

After about 18 months, Nathan began to trust his treatment team, and his family had begun working hard on their role in his recovery and journey toward wellness. His mother, still geographically distant, entered psychotherapy, and his father and stepmother participated in individual therapy, family therapy, and weekly multifamily group therapy. A significant investment of money, time, energy, and emotion were necessary ingredients that allowed Nathan to become well.

Nathan began experiencing members of his treatment team as loving, fun, and on his side, which built trust and allowed him to let down his guard and talk about his hurts, pains, fears, and weaknesses. During the process of opening up and making himself vulnerable, he experienced validation, a sense of "feeling felt." Nathan experienced relief from his own self-judgment, which allowed him to view himself as a lovable and valuable person, a process that took many years to fully play out. Ultimately, however, those of us on his treatment team were able to witness his change and his process of becoming well.

Over the course of his treatment, Nathan's IWM was rewritten and neurologically rewired. As his affect regulation system was slowly rebuilt, he began to become unstuck developmentally. Nathan continued to struggle in new situations such as finding a job and believing he could succeed. However, he worked hard and developed more self-efficacy. Over time, he became less fearful and anxious and more confident, growing into a young man who wanted to be seen as a whole person and not only a strong, muscular guy.

The Window of Tolerance

In order to prevent relapse and for recovery to occur, it is essential that adolescents and young adults build their capacity to tolerate various levels of arousal. Some newly recovering individuals within these age groups can be emotionally reactive. As they attempt to regulate their emotional states, they are emotionally hijacked and find themselves outside the *window of tolerance*. Hyper-aroused and reactive, their autonomic nervous system (ANS) is biologically tilted on the side of sympathetic arousal. In this state, many become emotionally flooded, impulsive, aggressive, and experience racing thoughts. Overall, they are reactive. In this state, the emotional excitatory regions of the brain (amygdala) are overriding the higher level rational, logical, inhibitory regions of the brain (prefrontal cortex). Young people in this state may then act out their emotions, absent of consideration of the impact, ramifications, and consequences of their behavior on themselves and others.

Others are on the opposite end of the spectrum, although still outside the window of tolerance. These teens are disconnected from their internal emotional experiences, physiological states, and are "stuffing" and minimizing emotions. Many are driven by their internal emotional experiences, but they are unable to *recognize* the connection between arousal, thinking, and behavior. They are lacking the ability to articulate the connection. These young people are alexithymic (unable to recognize emotion or use words to express their feelings), hypo-aroused, and dismissive. Biologically their ANS is tilted on the side of parasympathetic arousal. They often can appear collapsed, cognitively slowed, numb, lethargic, passive, or depressed (4).

It is interesting that each of the steps in 12-step programs deals with getting rid of shame and guilt. We have seen that shame is a powerful emotion that can trigger a young person's fall out of the window of tolerance.

The Modulation Model

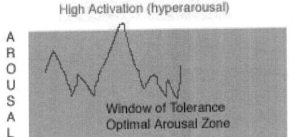

High Activation (hyperarousal)

A
R
O
U
S
A
L

Window of Tolerance
Optimal Arousal Zone

Low Activation (hyparousal)

Ogden & Minton (2000)

In early sobriety, clinicians work hard to build capacity for affect regulation, part of which comes from increasing the clients' tolerable range of arousal. This builds their capacity to tolerate different levels of arousal without being emotionally hijacked into an ANS sympathetic state. In addition, this work also builds their capacity to stay connected to their emotional and physiological states without being numb, repressed, or disconnected into a parasympathetic state of hypo-arousal. Overall, the task for clients working with therapists is to increasingly develop the ability to stay within the window of tolerance.

Young people in early recovery must develop a vocabulary for emotions so that they can identify and discern what they are feeling and label it. They then learn to allow themselves to experience emotions physiologically, and talk about where they feel it in their body. Once these emotions are expressed, these teens and adolescents can collaborate with others in order to form effective coping tools.

For adolescents and young adults, this stage of development and maturation is important for a successful life in all areas, but for those recovering from drug use, affect regulation and turning to others for co-regulation are both essential to promote recovery and prevent relapse. Some of the signs and symptoms of relapse (5) include:

- Emotional overreaction
- Starting to experience serious sensitivity to stress
- No longer telling others what they are thinking and feeling, they instead try to convince themselves and others that everything is all right, when it is not
- They avoid those who will give them honest feedback and/or become irritable and angry with them
- They notice that ordinary, everyday problems become overwhelming and no matter how hard they try, they cannot solve their problems
- They start feeling "down-in-the dumps" and have very low energy
- They use sex, food, drugs, work, gambling, and so forth, to regulate their affective states rather than turning to others

Although many warning signs and symptoms of relapse exist, it is easy to see that affect dysregulation is the common theme linking them.

Chapter 8: Notes

1. Schore, A.N. *Attachment & Human Development* Vol 2 No 1 April 2000 23-47.

2. Schore, A.N. *Affect Dysregulation and Disorders of the Self.* (New York, W.W. Norton, 2003).

3. Siegel, D. J. *The Developing Mind* (The Guildford Press, 1999).

4. Ogden, Pat, K. Minton, C. *Pain, Trauma and the Body* (New York, Norton Books, 2006).

5. (2010) http://www.drug-rehabilitation.com/relapse_signs. htm.

Chapter 9
Implications for Treatment

Before chemical dependent individuals can become attached to treatment, they must first get detached from the object of their addiction (1).

When it comes to working with young people with substance abuse and other issues, some division exists among clinicians about when and where to start the treatment process. Clinicians trained exclusively in mental health might subscribe to the idea that if they address underlying issues, then the drugs will not be needed for soothing and users will relinquish their use. On the other hand, clinicians trained in the addiction field often disagree, believing that drug use creates consequences for the user; if the addicted individuals quit using, then their problems will go away and their life will return to normal. Both see clients and their issues through the prism of their training.

Clinicians well trained in the assessment, diagnosis, and treatment of mental health issues might not be trained in addiction. However, as previously noted, the *Diagnostic and Statistical Manual of Mental Disorders* (DSM IV) devotes more pages to substance use disorders than any other disorder. In addition, the DSM IV states that clinicians must rule out medical and drug use issues before diagnosing any other disorder. I mention this again because many clinicians are not required to take courses on assessing, diagnosing, and treating substance use disorders in either their undergraduate or graduate school programs.

Sadly, many clinicians, like most parents of teens and young adults, received their information about adolescent and young adult drug use from their own experience with drugs as a young person. Those taking courses on substance use disorders are typically taught about the etiology and treatment of these disorders, using the adult model of addiction/alcoholism, although we know juvenile-onset substance use is very different from adult onset. For example, the progression of the illness can be significantly more rapid for teenagers than adults; adults primarily use one drug, but young people typically use multiple drugs. In addition, unlike adults, adolescents and young adults do not have a fully developed brain and body.

As mentioned earlier, mental health clinicians who have been trained in the treatment of depression, anxiety, relational, and developmental issues could overlook or minimize drug use when treating adolescent clients. Or, these clinicians could overly focus on the mental health issues or psycho-social issues and minimize substance use as either not particularly important or one that will go away once the underlying mental health issues are resolved. This approach ignores the fact that substance abuse can take on a life of its own as users' relationship to intoxication grows and is detrimental to health, mental health, school, family, sports, friendships, emotional and social development, and life in general.

For their part, addiction counselors often receive extensive training in assessing, diagnosing, and treating substance abuse disorders and codependency issues. Often passionate about helping individuals and families troubled by these problems, this group of treatment providers has often experienced personal struggles with addiction. Many find a program of recovery that gives them a great gift in understanding and helping others suffering from similar issues.

Training for addiction counselors is heavily rooted in the 12-step philosophy, which first appeared in 1935 and was developed and introduced by addicted individuals, primarily because the medical and therapeutic communities failed to effectively treat alcoholism and addiction. A large majority of addiction counselors are trained in the "disease concept" of addiction, rooted in the work from biostatistician, physiologist, and alcoholism researcher, EM Jellineck. His research influenced the American Medical Association's decision to classify alcoholism as a disease. Later studies suggested that genetics can be a significant variable in determining the likelihood of individuals developing alcoholism. Advances in technology led to the so-called "decade of the brain" (the 1990s), and subsequent research supported the idea that alcoholism is rooted in biology. Despite scientific progress, however, many certified addiction counselors are not trained in juvenile-onset substance-use disorders or mental health issues.

Mental health counselors are sometimes frustrated by what they view as addiction counselors' over-focus on drugs as the cause of disruption in drug-users' lives, which they see as enabling mental health issues because they are left undiagnosed and untreated. Likewise, certified drug counselors often see mental health counselors as overly focused on the mental health issues, thereby minimizing or overlooking the significance of their clients' drug use.

In reality, practitioners in both fields are correct. People are complicated, and as suggested throughout this book, a bio-psycho-social interplay takes place that influences our thoughts, emotions, personality, biology, and behavior. Like gears in a clock, they are all equally important and moving off of one another. In order to effectively help individuals surrender their addiction and develop their capacity for healthy attachment and regulation, we need to educate, guide, and support the whole person, along with surrounding social systems. Until substance abusers can grow from their insecure (avoidant, disorganized, or ambivalent) attachment organization to a healthy "earned secure" attachment, they remain vulnerable to other addictions such as compulsive overeating/food, work, sex, spending, gambling, image, and so forth, for regulation. Therefore, developing the client's capacity for secure attachment is of significant importance throughout the recovery process. However, we also address the need for an order of operations as we approach the addicted client.

We need to remember that internally, substance addiction influences adolescent and young adult thinking, perceptions, attitudes, values, emotions, personality, and neurological development. This influence then negatively affects their behavior in ways that can be observed and measured in school, work, family, friendships, sports, antisocial/illegal behavior, and finances. Addiction develops deeply and broadly—and with great speed. It takes very little time to disrupt users' lives. In addition, the relationship to intoxication is reinforced with every use. Because of these factors, the relationship to intoxication must first be disrupted so the impact of addiction is stopped and future negative consequences of drug use are prevented. At that point, clients can become open to treatment.

Flores states: *Abstinence must be the first goal of recovery. Clinicians who work with this population on a sustained basis know how difficult it is to form a working therapeutic alliance with a practicing alcoholic or addict. Before chemically dependent individuals can become attached to treatment, they must first get detached from the object of their addiction* (2).

The Six Stages of Recovery

As the old saying goes *"You can lead a horse to water but you can't make him drink."* Addicts are often like the horse that does not know he is thirsty and that water is right there in front of him, yet the system around the addict is saying *drink*! The purpose of the intervention phase of treatment is to help addicts recognize they are thirsty and water is in front of them.

As the common misconception goes, drug users must first hit bottom and want help before they can be helped. However, teens and young adults with a pathological relationship to intoxication are not supposed to recognize their use as a problem, want to quit, and seek help. It goes against their diagnosis to see their drug use as a problem. In early treatment therapists working with individuals and their families lift the bottom, so to speak, in order to help users begin to recognize their use as a problem. Acknowledging that drugs create negative consequences in one's life is the first step; wanting a new life free from drugs, drug culture, and addiction is close to the last. The six stages of recovery help illuminate the way drug users' motivation to change will develop through the recovery process.

Recognition:

A problem cannot be fixed until it is recognized. For drug users, the Recognition stage occurs when they begin seeing that drug use is creating consequences in the areas of school, family, friendships, sports, work, money, goals, and so forth. Despite the consequences, users often blame other things for their negative circumstances, i.e., "My grades are falling because my teacher doesn't like me." Rarely do young people connect negative events or consequences to their drug use.

The first goal of treatment involves helping teens and young adults inventory the link between their drug use and consequences, which then helps them to recognize it as a problem. The motivation to show up to treatment often comes as a result of law enforcement ordering treatment or their families threatening consequences if they do not agree to treatment. Young people show up for treatment only because they have to be there. But they are not alone. Adults do not start treatment because they want to, but because law enforcement, employers, or spouses have made it clear that the user must get help "or else."

Admission:

When drug-using teens and young adults view their drug use as fun, exciting, a way to enhance to social relationships, and a source of soothing, early treatment makes them look at their drug use differently. As they move through the recognition stage and start to own how their use is hurting both them and the people who love them the most, they start to "get it," thereby moving to the Admission stage. This happens not just on a vacillating intellectual level, but at visceral gut level. They start to recognize it as a fact, not just an idea. With this deep connection to the reality of their drug problem comes some grief and loss as these young people become aware it is time to let go of their relationship to intoxication. During this period, they often fear they will not be able to experience future good times in their life, so they grieve the good times intoxication created. They reluctantly let go of their drug friends and drug culture and grieve this loss, as they also fear the possibility that they might find life boring—they even wonder if they will become boring, too. At this stage they are still in treatment because they are required to be there.

Seeking Help:

By this time in early sobriety, young clients have a new perspective on their drug use, gleaned from what they learned during the Recognition and Admission stages of recovery. Specifically, in reaching the Seeking Help stage they recognize the need to stay clean, although most still face temptations to use. Many are still in the process of moving on from the familiar drug culture, but they now show up to treatment because they have acknowledged the need to do so and not simply because they have to.

Acceptance:

The Acceptance stage in recovery occurs when users no longer bargain with their treatment plan, as in saying, "I don't think I really need to go to meetings. I can stay clean by just working more." Moreover, in the Acceptance phase, users have moved through the grief and loss of ending their relationship to intoxication and drug culture. Furthermore, they can talk about their illness of drug addiction without shame and show up to treatment because they are aware they need this help. In the Recognition and Admission stages users *comply* with what is expected of them, but in subsequent stages users stay clean with an internal *conviction* that they need to be sober.

Volition:

In the Volition stage of recovery, users want treatment and participate in therapy, 12-step meetings, group therapy, working with a sponsor on the steps, and so forth, because they want to. Not only has there been deep internal discovery of recovery, but users experience the benefits of being free from addiction and cultivating new and fulfilling relationships with people who allow them to be themselves and be seen. They also pursue new passions and healthy activities in life.

Conversion:

The Conversion stage means that users now have a new life. No longer a slave to addiction, former users are free to create a happier life and have ceased struggling over being an addict or needing help. No longer grieving the loss of their relationship to intoxication, they have new-found confidence, coping skills, passions, and healthy attachments in their life.

The goal of therapy involves severing users' pathological relationship to intoxication, while inviting them into an instructional therapeutic relationship in order to build their capacity for affect regulation and to develop and negotiate healthy attachments. However, reaching these goals is contingent on first recognizing the problem.

Breaking Down Denial—the Role of the Clinician

Given that adolescents and young adults start treatment because they have to, we expect to see a lack of excitement about being there. They might come into the office and show passive-aggressive behavior, i.e., avoiding eye contact and giving minimal responses to assessment questions. It is helpful to accept these young clients and meet them where they are.

In the graduate school course I teach on addiction, I have students engage in role-playing exercises. In one exercise, I walk into the classroom as the teen showing up to addiction treatment for the first time. This exercise grabs students' attention about the importance of understanding where clients are coming from, so that counselors can properly attune to the clients as they are.

I arrange the classroom in a U-shaped fashion, which allows me to approach each student playing the role of clinician while I stay in the role of a teen saying: "It's so dumb that I have to be here in counseling. I don't have a problem, my parents do. I don't want to talk about drugs—they're not a problem."

Acting as clinicians, how could my students best respond to this encounter? Many students feel a pressure to perform and magically break down denial right away. They believe it is what they are mandated to do. Others mentally review previous graduate school readings to determine their approach based on a theoretical textbook framework. Some trust their instincts and attune to the client.

Those eager to break denial and help clients recognize their use as a problem might respond with, "You're in denial," or, "You need to get clean because it is affecting your family and your potential." Those students who search their minds for a theory to guide them might look lost for a minute, but then they

194

say something like, "Do you think you have a problem with drugs?" or "How do you feel about coming to counseling?"

The teen or young adult user usually responds to these approaches along the lines of, "I don't think it's a problem and I shouldn't be here."

The role play I engage in with students captures the attention of those at a loss for ways to help the newly sober young addict. Usually, students who are calm, unhurried, intuitive, and who trust their instincts are able to attune and instead of reaching for a response, they let one come to them.

An attuned response is possible for clients who need to "feel felt" and be met where they are; young people need this attunement before they can move forward in their therapeutic process. "I really get that you must be pissed off about having to be here today," the counselor could say. "It sounds like you are not seeing drug use as a problem in your life and yet your parents are dragging you here to address a drug problem. I think I'd be pretty frustrated, angry, and bummed out, too. I might even be a bit resentful." That response begins an attuned relationship in which the client initially has the experience of "feeling felt" by the therapists.

Clinicians who want to hurry to break down denial and who are unaccustomed to dealing with resistant teenagers and young adults might fear that this response is tantamount to "co-signing" or colluding with denial. But that is not the case. This attuned response does not imply that young clients do not have a drug problem, but it does allow clinicians to convey understanding of the emotional and intellectual challenge of entering treatment. In early childhood development, individuals need attunement and trust to develop, and young people need these same ingredients to begin the therapeutic process. When clients have the experience of being understood they are able to be open to future education and exploration within the therapeutic relationship.

Helping Clients Reach Their Own Conclusions about Drug Use
Intervention is a process not an event (3).

As the quote implies, intervention with adolescents and young adults is not a single event. Many have tried to convince drug users that they have a problem and need to get help to get sober, but they quickly learned that their concern and insight are not met with gratitude. Insightful intervention does not lead users to view drug use as a problem, and users typically continue to maintain their stance that no problem exists. They protect their relationship to intoxication by rationalizing, justifying, and minimizing it. As therapists, our role involves working with individuals and families in ways that help users conclude that using drugs is problematic.

It is fascinating to watch young people with addiction issues try to view drugs as an issue. So often, even when they try, they cannot see the problems. Intervention into a client's belief about drug use can occur after the therapist has worked through initial resistance and has established a relationship. For example, I ask clients to dig deep and take an open look at how their drug use has created consequences. Nonresistant and open clients stare at their lap for a moment while they take a mental inventory of the consequences of their drug use. Then they look up and say something like: "It's created problems in the relationship with my parents. They don't trust me as much as they used to. It has caused me to not care about school as much. Some of my friends tell me they're worried about my use."

When I reinforce these introspective efforts and acknowledge the users' openness and willingness to look at this issue, I ask if they can think of more consequences of drug use. Generally, they come up with only one additional example. Even when trying hard, they manage to come up with three or four examples. However, later, when we have made it through the intervention phase of treatment, they can articulate 25 to 30 different consequences. When they can do that, they are like the proverbial horse that has finally arrived at the water.

Getting the Horse to Water

For the intervention component of treatment in our outpatient services at Recovery Happens Counseling Services (www.recoveryhappens.com) my colleagues and I use a program drawn from *Effective Outpatient Treatment for Adolescents,* written by David Gust and Ted Smith. David Gust, a close colleague, mentor, and friend, has used and taught this model since the mid 1980s. I have used it since the mid-90s. His book offers an extremely comprehensive program model for working with young people and their families. Specifically, I have found the Chemical Use Assessment (CUA) particularly valuable when working to help clients reach their own conclusions about their problem and the need for sobriety.

The CUA is a guide that allows clinicians to collaboratively explore ways substance use has created consequences in their clients' lives in the following life areas: school, family, friends, sports, work, money, legal, health, mental health, spirituality, sexuality, and relationship to self and community. Within each area, clients explore specific drug-related incidents that created consequences and identify how they felt about it at the time or looking back on it now. This process requires clinicians to have a battery of questions that might help elicit clients' thoughtful inventories. For example, questions about school would include:

- Have you ever gone to school high?
- How often do you go to school high?
- Have you bought or sold drugs on campus?

197

- Have you ever skipped school to get high? Been late to school because you were high or coming down off of drugs?
- Do you have a reputation among your peers as a drug user at school?
- How have your classmates expressed concern? Have teachers expressed concern?
- Have you told yourself you were going to do your homework, but you got high and either did not do it or did not do a good job? How has your GPA changed since you started using?
- Have you ever tried to quit or cut back on your drug use because you saw it affecting school? Have you attended school dances, sporting events, or other activities under the influence?

Some responses allow clinicians to come up with even more exploratory questions. Then, as clients acknowledge that they relate to the questions, clinicians ask for specific examples of what happened and how they felt about it at the time or looking back on it from the current perspective. Clinicians then record on paper the responses in their clients' own words before moving on to other life areas. When the CUA is complete and both clients and clinicians can't come up with more negative consequences, then the clients' responses are typed up and they can review it during the next session.

With a list of negative consequences in front of them, clients can respond to questions about reactions that come up. What new insights do they have? Or how would they feel if they read this about someone else—their brother, sister, mother, or a friend? What would they think if they read this information about another kid at school they did not know other than what is written on the paper? What would they recommend for this kid? What predictions would they make if this kid kept using? Finally, the next step is convening a family session where the young people share the inventory with their parents.

Dishonesty is the currency of adolescent drug use. Moreover, not talking about addiction is a common rule in households with addiction or alcoholism issues. So sharing this inventory with family members opens up communication and promotes honesty, accountability, and responsibility for recovery. The inventory frees teens and young adults from the burden of their secrets and breaks through their parents' lingering denial. In addition, the inventory moves clients past the intellectual recognition of the problem to gut-level understanding. Clinicians cannot violate clients' confidentiality, but they also cannot collude with secret-keeping rules so pervasive in families with addictions. However, clinicians can create the safe space necessary for the teens and their families to share perceptions about the problems brought about by drug use.

When clients share their history and consequences of drug use, then parents also share their perception of what consequences have already affected their child's life, but they do so without lecturing, put downs, judgment. An established rule holds that our clients cannot be punished for anything they share. We also acknowledge the courage it takes to face the consequences of drug use with themselves and their parents. By using this process, we take clients from:

- not seeing their drug use as a problem, to
- talking with their therapists about how it is a problem, and then
- reading their own words on paper about the problem, and
- sharing the reality of the problem with their families, and finally,
- family members share their perceptions of the drug use as a problem

At this point the client's denial has been challenged and the horse is at the water.

Exploring the ways drugs have influenced past thinking, perceptions, attitudes, choices, and consequences can induce shame and guilt. However, as explained earlier, shame and guilt can inhibit the dopamine system and create a sense of wanting to be "unseen." In young people with limited capacity for affect regulation, experiencing shame and guilt can drive addiction. The clinician's role is to allow clients to be connected to the affect related to their past. Clinicians do this while simultaneously offering clients a relationship that offers a secure base to risk exploring the consequences, be seen, and learn from their experiences while making sense of them. However, they can have this experience without being flooded by the emotions or left alone with the feelings, which might leave them dismissive and avoidant. Here, clinicians offer a relationship characterized with empathy, attunement, nonjudgment, a focus on feelings, and understanding. This relationship also models healthy attachment and offers a co-regulating container for affect regulation.

The CUA is an intellectual tool that enables clients to see their drug use as a problem, but it is the relationship with the counselor that offers a healthy relationship that is internalized and becomes the secure base for ongoing exploration and trust in relationships. Although the experiences in relationships shaped the neurological and psychological structure of the IWM, this new relationship with the therapist offers the corrective experience by rewriting the IWM.

The Family Has a Role

At some point, families realize that they alone cannot help their children, which prompts them to pick up the phone and ask for help. Likewise, therapists cannot break down denial alone, and they need families to learn how they have participated in the illness and see their new role in their children's wellness. Parents have a significant role in the process of breaking down denial and are key players in working through attachment issues.

Essential for the clinician treating young people, the family component of treatment creates the expectations for the family to work with clinicians and not against them. For example, going home to a family where there is active drug use, emotional dysregulation, and relational traumas, works against the therapeutic process with teens and young adults. Of course, it is not the family's role to recognize these issues on their own, but the treatment provider can educate and support family members.

After many years of providing education to parents on this topic in our programs, I co-authored the 2006 book, *How to Help Your Child Become Drug Free: A Guide for Parents of Adolescents and Young Adults with Substance Abuse or Addiction* (4), available at my website: www.recoveryhappens.com. Given to every family in our program, this book is a core component of treatment programs and providers in the U.S. and Canada. It is also used in college courses on addiction.

What we Cover in the Family Component of Treatment

Rather than the addict hitting bottom, we have seen that the system around the addict has to hit bottom first. Put another way, if the system around addicts does not hit bottom, then the system will not develop the boundaries needed to "lift the bottom" for addicts. When the family system gets to the point at which they cannot tolerate their child's drug use, they will implement boundaries that help the child see the drug use as a problem. At that point, teenagers and those who have reached young adulthood begin to recognize the benefits of quitting, even if initially, it is to get parents off their back.

When, for example, the family system tolerates and condones the use of alcohol and marijuana, but not oxycontin or cocaine, then they get a child who quits using those two drugs, but continues to use marijuana and alcohol. When the family system becomes emotionally, relationally, and financially ripped off enough (system hitting bottom) by their child's alcohol and marijuana abuse/addiction, then they will step up their boundaries and include formerly tolerated substances. At this point, they begin to see that their teenage or young adult child is not addicted to a particular drug, but to intoxication itself. From that understanding, family members are in a position to stop participating in the illness through their own denial and enabling. They then can participate in their child's recovery, starting with seeking help and defining good boundaries at home.

Common Family Denial
Rationalizing:

"Kids will be kids... It is a phase of life... It is a rite of passage... Boys will be boys... I used when I was a kid and I out grew it... All kids use..."

These statements justify and make excuses for young people who use drugs, and also imply that it is somehow okay. Interestingly, in addition to parents, some mental health professionals, pediatricians, nurses, probation officers, police officers, coaches, school administrators, and so forth, may also participate in denial.

Minimizing:

"It's only marijuana... It's only alcohol... At least he's still in school... At least she hasn't been arrested... He's not as bad as Jimmy..."

Minimizing discounts the severity of use and the consequences that have occurred as a result of use.

Common Enabling Behaviors in Families

We need to educate families about the way enabling prevents users from experiencing the logical consequences of their use. For example, if young people are arrested for drinking and driving, then logical consequences include sitting in juvenile hall or jail, paying fines, and doing community service or a work project. Experiencing these consequences works to penetrate the users' denial and helps them recognize problems created by their drug use. But rescuing users from the consequences enables denial to continue and in the long run, contributes to the problem.

Examples of Rescuing:

- Hiring defense attorneys
- Bailing teen and young adult users out of jail
- Paying off drug debts
- Doing users' chores for them
- Doing users' homework for them

Family Boundaries

Clinicians working with drug users have a role in helping the family develop healthy boundaries at home, thereby preventing further enabling. These boundaries also intervene in the child's relationship to intoxication. Chapter 5 of the aforementioned book, *How to Help Your Child Become Drug Free*, goes into great detail about family boundaries and offers a working model that families and clinicians can use immediately. Healthy boundaries can include the following expectations:

- Abstinence from all drugs and alcohol
- Following through with drug testing
- No drugs or paraphernalia on our property
- No friends allowed on our property if they are under the influence of drugs or alcohol
- Mandatory enrollment in a program or counseling program that addresses the teen's drug use

Consequences for unmet expectations vary from family to family but can include:

- Grounding, restricted to the house
- Loss of electronics
- Loss of driving privileges
- Loss of phone
- Suspension of teens' allowance

For young adults, consequences could include loss of all financial support for phone, car, school costs, and housing. Finally, the most important element is having families on the same page and willing to follow through with their expectations.

Parents as a Resource for Their Child

Part of the ongoing process in therapy involves helping parents work on being attuned to their child. For parents trying to understand this concept, I recommend Dan Siegel's book, *Parenting from the Inside Out*. Being attuned empowers parents to be a resource in their child's life. As discussed earlier, a child with a sense that a parent really "gets me," has a parent who is a resource for affect regulation, a model for empathy, and a model for negotiating relationships. Being attuned caregivers is critical when asking children to let go of a relationship to intoxication, because during this time, young people need a healthy, real relationship to turn to. When young people let go of a relationship to intoxication, they are without their defenses, social skills, or affect regulation tools. They are going through grief and loss as they break away from their relationship to intoxication and begin to reorganize friends, activities, their thinking, and so forth.

Parents do not control their children's drug use; they are powerless over their children's decisions about drug use and intoxication. Parents can set boundaries, but the teens and young adults make the choice to abide by those boundaries. However, parents have control over how they model introspection, accountability, affect regulation, and negotiating relationships.

Attachment offers empowerment, and it is a misinterpretation to think of attachment as something in the past, a process that has already happened. This thinking results in parental guilt. When parents see that their relationship today can influence the way their children mature into adults, this helps them see where they still have power.

Chapter 9: Notes

1. Flores, *Addiction as an Attachment Disorder*. (The Rowman & Littlefield Publishing Group, Inc., 2004).

2. Flores, 2004.

3. Gust, Smith. *Effective Outpatient Treatment for Adolescents: a program model for counselors and therapists working with adolescents experiencing alcohol and other drug-related problems*. (Produced by FinishLine, Shingle Springs, CA, 2008).

4. Gust, Walker, Daily, *How to Help Your Child Become Drug Free: A Guide for Parents of Adolescents & Young Adults with Substance Abuse or Addiction*. (Produced by FinishLine, Shingle Springs, CA, 2006).

Chapter 10
Case Studies

Although I have included case studies throughout the book, I want to conclude with a closer look at teens and young people who have experienced the painful consequences of drug and alcohol abuse, but are now in the process of rebuilding their lives in recovery. As you will see, a range of severity exists, but it is as important to adequately treat the teen on the road to addiction as it is to treat a complex case of dual diagnosis.

Case Study 1:
RJ: *Nip it in the bud: Using only once warrants counseling*

RJ, age 14, came into counseling as a result of his parents finding out that he used marijuana for the first time. When his parents called, they said that they wanted to "nip it in the bud," but were unsure if he should be enrolled into outpatient treatment. This is a common sign of the ambivalence parents experience when they discover their young child has just tried drugs. So many parents want to intervene, but at the same time they do not want to overreact.

I assured RJ's mother that any kid who has used even once is in need of outpatient treatment. She asked why outpatient treatment is warranted in such a case. I pointed out that an evaluation would help to determine if her son really had used only once, or if their discovery was the tip of a small or larger iceberg. I also maintained that even if he was a one-time user, he still needed outpatient care—not inpatient or intensive outpatient (IOP), but rather once a week sessions where a particular treatment scenario could take place.

What we did for RJ and his family is the same as we do for any family whose child is using drugs, regardless if it is only once or once a day. The difference is that the treatment for a guy like RJ is going to be less complex, less sophisticated, and much less time consuming than for the guy who uses every day. Treatment is equally needed in both cases.

First, RJ was evaluated to determine the extent of his use. During the short course of treatment we uncovered that he used marijuana twice and alcohol three times and that was the extent of his use. RJ did not have any history of mental health or family dynamic issues. His family relationships, mental health status, and school history were all within normal limits of his age and stage of psycho-social development.

After our assessments were completed, RJ received education about the different stages of drug use, the progression from experimentation, misuse, abuse, and addiction. He learned about denial and how that shows up for young people in the form of minimizing, such as saying "It's only alcohol" or "It's only marijuana." These statements serve only to discount the severity of what has already happened and the risks of what could occur if drug use continues. He learned about the denial defenses, such as rationalizing, and came to understand that saying things like *everyone uses, it's a phase of life, or a rite of passage, or kids will be kids* are no more than statements and mindsets to justify using. He understood the concepts.

Subsequently, during treatment RJ became educated about the risks associated with alcohol, marijuana, and other trendy drugs abused by teens. After the education component was finished, we dove a little bit deeper to examine the consequences of use specific to him. He learned that he had spent money on using, money that was supposed to be used for other things. He also connected his use to fracturing his relationship with his parents, primarily by eroding trust. He admitted he lied to his parents about the extent of his use and also felt as if he had started to gravitate more toward other drug-using friends, but now he can see where that was headed. This was a four week process itself, and when we were finished uncovering any and all subtle or large consequences he experienced from his use, the list was typed up so he could process it.

RJ was asked to read aloud to his counselor his chemical use history and the subsequent consequences. Then RJ processed what he read, becoming increasingly aware that he made a mistake to start using drugs; the brief work he had done so far allowed him to connect to himself, as well as reconnect with his parents.

During this time his parents also attended the parent education class and learned about the trendy drugs and their effects. They also developed a good home contract that set clear boundaries about being drug free. In addition, they learned how to drug test at home and to make sure that they would not participate in his illness through parental denial or enabling behaviors, such as rescuing him from drug-related consequences or making excuses for his drug use. Finally, they also formulated a kind of summary of the way RJ experienced drug-related consequences: RJ had been grounded for a week, had to start counseling, be randomly drug tested, and had lost trust for a little while with his family.

We then had a family session at which RJ presented to his parents his drug use history and the associated consequences. In that same session, his parents presented how they saw drug use creating consequences for RJ.

During this time, RJ had been drug tested and was clean on all drug screens. In addition, he had no mental health or family dynamic issues, so we only had to finalize a home contract that clearly stated that he would be randomly drug tested and if he had drugs or drug paraphernalia, he would experience consequences for it.

By the end of this 8-10 week process, we saw the family reconnected and on the same page. RJ's drug use was stopped, plus he was educated about drugs and their effects on developing teens; he had explored how his use had already created consequences in his life and he was connected to that experience. In addition, he had to share his drug use history and the associated consequences with his parents and his parents shared their perceptions with him. His parents learned how to avoid enabling behaviors, and instead, establish clear boundaries and carry out ongoing drug testing. On follow up, RJ went on to develop normally and he never needed to return to treatment.

RJ's case reflects a fairly normal, healthy family with a healthy kid who had started to make bad choices; however, early intervention combined with coming from a healthy family turned it around. This case is also very important in that many programs and counselors might have dismissed the importance of treatment and the components of what was needed for a teen like RJ, even in a case of one-time use. Again, research indicates that the younger someone is when they first experience intoxication and subsequently develop a pathological relationship to intoxication, the more likely they are to develop addiction and/or other mental health disorders. In the absence of this early intervention, it is likely that RJ would have been another statistic.

Case Study 2
JR: "Self Medication" Case Study: *I used because I needed to, not because I wanted to.*

JR was a likable 17-year-old. Quiet, polite, well mannered, and with a calm temperament that made him easy to connect with. He was not game playing or disconnected from how he felt, nor was he an angry, macho, out to prove himself as a "cool" type of kid, although he did not communicate how he was really feeling on the inside. His parents called because he had been increasingly withdrawing from school work and family interactions over the last year. His girlfriend of three years even expressed concern to his family about how inward he had become; he did not seem to care about things as much as he once had. She also told his parents that other friends had told her JR had been drinking and using marijuana the last year. They came to her out of their concern for their good friend, showing that JR had a community that witnessed these changes in him.

JR came from a conservative family who lived in the country, 45 miles from our office. His dad was a hardworking businessman in the insurance industry and his mother was a homemaker who was active in the kids' schools and in her church and community activities.

JR did not know how his parents found out about his use, but they communicated that a good source told them. At that point, they believed they needed to get help as a family and brought him in for treatment.

At first JR was upset with his parents, but then complied with the family's expectation that he enter counseling. JR was open about using drugs, admitting that he had started using marijuana on occasion over the last year, and also used alcohol infrequently. However, his alcohol consumption had been on the rise, going from once a month to two to three times a week, plus he had developed a history of blackouts. He used with some friends on occasion, but he did not want other friends to know because he knew they would disapprove. JR denied any other drug use.

JR had no family history of alcohol or drug abuse, although his mother thought her brother was likely alcoholic, but since JR's uncle had never been medically diagnosed or sought treatment, this was only her opinion. JR denied any history of mental health issues or counseling.

We started treatment with JR, and the parents attended the parent education class. His parents also worked to formulate their perceptions of the problem so they could present it in a family session when the counselor said the time was right. They also started drug testing, went to community support groups, and implemented boundaries in the home.

JR was compliant. He came to weekly sessions, followed through with drug testing, processed the education, and started to explore the ways his use created consequences. However, as time went on, JR started to talk about feeling depressed. In fact, he believed he had been depressed for the past two years. Although he could not pinpoint the source of his depression, he acknowledged that using was a vehicle to feel better.

When he let go of the drugs he appeared a bit brighter in affect and color, pace of speech, and so on, but he was not happy. Because of the depression, he was still stuck in this low place, despite getting off drugs. At that point, he felt his emotions more, making his insecurity and depression difficult to manage and work through. We tried working through it initially by talking about physical exercise and identifying cognitive distortions. Again, he was compliant, but still did not feel better. Finally he relapsed after 90 days of sobriety; this sent him into a downward spiral of shame and a sense of powerlessness that made him want to hide and be "unseen." Then to make things worse, his girlfriend broke up with him because of his history of covering up his drug use in their relationship.

Already depressed and limited in coping skills to handle losing his long term relationship, JR took a bottle of aspirin in a suicide attempt. Luckily, his mother came to check on him after dinner to make sure he did his homework, and she discovered him passed out in bed with the aspirin bottle next to him. She called 911 and JR was rushed to the local hospital. He was given charcoal and his stomach was pumped to prevent any more absorption of what he ingested and to empty his stomach altogether.

JR stayed in the hospital for three days and was put on an antidepressant, the first time he had taken any psychiatric medication. I visited JR in the hospital to let him know I cared about him and his wellness and to make sure he knew I was still on his team. We continued to meet weekly for psychotherapy while he continued on his antidepressant. Very quickly, JR experienced relief as a result of the medication and counseling. In addition, as his family paid more attention to him and they became closer, JR appeared freer to be seen and show up to the relationship. No longer withdrawn from family and friends, he and his mom spoke at a school assembly about teen depression and how it led to his self-medicating. He then described the relief he experienced from taking the right medication, participating in his counseling sessions, and opening up in his relationships.

JR shows us what can happen when teens hide their depression and end up drawn to using street drugs to medicate undiagnosed and untreated depression. He was using drugs and alcohol not because he wanted to have fun like so many substance abusers and addicts, but because he needed to experience relief. He was a true self-medicator. It was fortunate that JR survived his aspirin overdose and was able to recover. This is a case where earlier detection of JR's internal unhappiness might have led to earlier treatments and prevented what could have been the end of his life.

Case Study 3
Vince: A More Complicated Dual Diagnosis

Vince, age 25, came into therapy seeking relief from his depression and anxiety. During our first session he walked somewhat sluggishly to the chair in my office. Then he lifted his head up slowly and explained that he felt alone and depressed and did not know what to do. The flow of energy in his mind was slower in Vince than in most other people. It took him a while to formulate his thoughts and then express them, along with receiving and processing information from me. Early on, his low energy was so clear that I knew how much courage it took to reach out and seek help.

As Vince started talking about his mental suffering, he cried and cried. He would apologize for crying, and in response, I empathically sent him love and compassion from my heart. It was one of those moments as a clinician in which I wanted my soul to talk to his soul—if such a thing could happen. My pace of interaction with Vince quickly became organized around his slow pace and soon we resonated with each other's rhythm as I acknowledged his suffering and courage. He was "feeling felt" and I could see that this simple attuned response to him was already creating some relief.

Feeling safe, Vince started to share that he had felt suicidal over 30 times in the previous year, and it was love for his parents that kept him from following through with suicide attempts. Vince was likeable, insightful, personable, bright, and easy to align with, but noticeably ill.

Vince was referred by his treatment team of a psychologist and a psychiatrist. He had not made progress with his mental health issues because he was inconsistent in taking prescribed medications; Vince was also abusing marijuana, opiates, benzodiazepines, marijuana, and alcohol.

Vince's treatment team also found him likable and worked hard to believe in his wellness. They also gave him the time he needed, but his already challenging case was confounded by his addiction, and, therefore, he was not moving forward in treatment. Vince wanted to be well and feel better and put together three to five days of sobriety; however, he suffered so much during periods of abstinence that he was driven to seek relief and eventually use drugs to ameliorate his anxiety and depression.

A true dual diagnosis case, treating Vince's addiction alone would not make him well. In fact, several years before, he had gone to a premiere out-of-state addiction treatment program and attended outpatient addiction treatment for aftercare. He had had years of sobriety in the past, and earned a BA in college. The entire time, though, his mental health was not fully understood or treated. According to Vince, he "gutted it out" until he finally was right back using street drugs for relief and some happiness.

As a child, Vince was raised by both parents and lived with his younger brother, who also struggled with the same issues. His father and mother were both successful in their careers and seemed to connect well with each other, but struggled with how to best understand and help their children. Both parents had a family history of anxiety, depression, and addiction.

Starting at an early age, Vince struggled with anxiety. He remembered being around age six when he began to be overwhelmed by crowds and loud noises. He recalls being paranoid about death, ruminating on death for several days after seeing death scenes in movies. In high school he maintained slightly above average grades, but described those years as very hard. He told me he obsessed about a high school girlfriend, who broke up with him for being "too clingy." The obsession lasted several months and he called and texted her so frequently her upset parents called the police to report his behavior.

In college it was the same story, but there he ruminated about how others were "truly smart" and he felt like an academic imposter. He dated some, but always felt self-conscious, inferior, and intimidated. This usually led to him becoming aloof around people, especially girls, but he would fantasize about being more charming and confident with them than he was. For income, he did some data entry work but was dissatisfied with that as well. However, despite these struggles he was able to earn his bachelor's degree, but that turned into a two-sided coin. On one side he got his degree and was proud of the accomplishment, but on the other side his family observed his ability to get his degree, leading them to minimize the suffering and internal issues he struggled with daily.

I consulted with Vince's other clinicians so we could decide as a team how to get the best outcome possible for this young man, who was clearly motivated to get better. His past compliance with various treatments demonstrated that he had the capacity to recover and he had been able to develop a significant amount of sobriety. Since he had earned his college degree, he was open and willing to work at an outpatient level of care.

The problem was that the outpatient level of care with a psychologist, psychiatrist, and addictions specialist did not provide an adequate container of support for change and overall wellness, even with individual and sometimes family counseling added to the mix. However, he would not be served by an inpatient chemical dependency program or an inpatient psychiatric hospital. Both would treat only half of what was going on. In addition, although many programs we discovered were marketing themselves as treating both, in reality they treated one or the other and then took a superficial approach to the other side of the treatment equation.

After researching and finally discovering the right program for Vince, we had a team and family session to explain Vince's capacity for wellness. We reviewed what had been tried at an intensive outpatient level of care with the treatment team, and then presented the idea that what he really needed was a true inpatient, dual diagnosis program. Vince chose to check himself in one week later.

During the first two weeks, Vince struggled with some ambivalence about being there. While he knew it was the right thing, he was easily overwhelmed with anxiety. Nonetheless, he stayed for two months and then came back to live in a transition home where he could work with us as a treatment team again.

At that point, Vince was doing well. He followed the medication schedule his psychiatrist gave him, along with other recommendations of his psychologist and addictions specialist. Finally, he enrolled in college courses again, but this time so that he could help youth who also struggled with mental health issues. For Vince, these were kids for whom he felt a great deal of compassion and he connected with them easily.

Today, he is two years sober, continues to receive support from the treatment team, and he is experiencing the joy of stability, relief, and being paid to do a meaningful job he loves.

Case Study 5
Sue: The Opiate Addict

Sue was a young adult who had graduated from high school the previous year, but she struggled to complete a semester of college. She had a tender heart and wanted to help people, and is close to her divorced parents and her long-term boyfriend. As a high school junior, Sue was diagnosed with depression, but was never treated for it with counseling or medications. Rather, her family thought she was just going through a phase. What Sue never mentioned at that time was that she was anxious, too, and using marijuana daily, cocaine once a month, Ecstasy infrequently, but added alcohol on those occasions. Now as a young adult she still suffered from anxiety and depression and her use progressed to oxycontin and heroin.

The good news was that as a young adult, she recognized her need for help and was able to be forthcoming with her family and treatment providers who consisted of her psychiatrist and me. Besides her boyfriend, Sue had little interaction with peers. While some kids almost always use drugs with their peers, Sue preferred to get the drugs and use them by herself or only with her boyfriend.

I asked Sue if she knew what purpose the opiate system served for humans, and she responded that she understood it helped to regulate pain and pleasure. I validated that she was correct, adding that it was also one of the core neurobiological underpinnings of attachment; during attuned experiences within relationships, the opiate system fires and reinforces the bond/connection. In those moments of "feeling felt" this system is built, sustained, and reinforced. Dopamine goes along for the ride in this example, too, by the way.

I then asked Sue how many relationships she had in which she felt able to truly be seen for all of her strengths, shames, struggles, and so forth. Her answer? Zero.

So we talked about what it was like to feel so alone with her struggles, and with her strengths as well. At some point she connected to our discussion, so I said something I pose to all opiate addicts who reach that place during our early sessions. I say that the feeling they experience in that moment, related to being seen and feeling felt and that feels so good, is the activation of opiate system within a meaningful relationship and interaction. I then ask: If you could have this experience in more relationships or trade this moment right now for drugs, what would you choose?

Like others, Sue said she would choose the relationship. I assured Sue that therein was our treatment plan. We would work with her and her family to help her feel felt, be seen, and find and cultivate other relationships that support her in that way.

So the short-term goal was to get on an opiate replacement medicine, and the long-term goal was to develop the capacity to build and negotiate the relationships that will be needed to get off the medicine and get into relationships for the activation of her opiate system. Sue, like so many others, felt clear and empowered by this. It made sense to her and her family and treatment started from that foundation we built in *session one*.

This chapter and book has illuminated the varied levels of complexity to the etiology, case formulation and what is involved for the best treatment outcomes. Unfortunately, adolescent and young adult addiction and dual diagnosis treatment as a study and practice is still in its adolescence. Addiction treatment for teens started in the late seventies, later dual diagnosis came along, and only recently young adult or "transitional age youth." As a matter of fact, young adults are far too understudied. We have a long way to go and I believe it will be necessary for us to keep our minds wide open to different ways of thinking about this pervasive illness. The "disease" concept of addiction as a theoretical framework for etiology, case formulation and treatment has been extremely helpful and is equally limiting to treating the whole person. We have to keep stretching our minds, hearts and souls to help this population. New neuroscience, especially as it relates to how relationships shape the brain and mind (interpersonal neurobiology) offers us something to be thinking about for many more years to come.